Praise for *DES Stories*

Margaret Lee Braun has compiled a compelling collection of interviews and photographs, which are an important contribution to the literature and understanding of the DES issue. *DES Stories* is an important book that allows the reader to understand the personal experiences and consequences of DES exposure.

— *Arthur L. Herbst, M.D., Professor and Chairman, Department of Obstetrics and Gynecology, University of Chicago*

These are the lives, the families, and the stories of DES. Reader, listen well. Science can only explain the biological damage. But the brave voices of *DES Stories* inspire us toward social change.

— *Sandra Steingraber, Ph.D., author of* Living Downstream: A Scientist's Personal Investigation of Cancer and the Environment

DES Stories moved me deeply. This is the book we've been waiting for—to tell the human story. It can move you to tears, and beyond, to action and healing.

— *Marlies Koster, health educator, DES Center The Netherlands*

DES Stories describes the journeys of just 40 of the millions of individuals and families affected by their exposure to diethylstilbestrol, providing voices and faces to tell the story of one of the most devastating corporate and medical mistakes of our time. Woven in these stories are important lessons to learn about coping, survival, life, and death.

— *Susan P. Helmrich, Ph.D., co-founder and co-chair, DES Cancer Network*

Nancy Stuart's photographs of DES families are uniquely informative and considerate. She reveals, with warmth and understanding, the emotional ties within family relationships in this complex story.

— *Paul Caponigro, photographer; author of* Landscape *and* Meditations in Light

DES Stories puts DES where it should be—in the middle of public and private discourse about hormones, technology, and our risk for chemical exposure. The power of these stories is the truth-telling about personal journeys that are intrinsically linked to a global phenomena.

— *John A. McLachlan, Ph.D., Professor of Environmental Studies and Director, Center for Bioenvironmental Research, Tulane/Xavier Universities*

It is impossible not to be moved, sometimes to tears, sometimes to cheers, by *DES Stories*. Margaret Lee Braun presents the aftereffects of DES exposure with compassion, humanity, and unflinching honesty. Nancy Stuart's photographs illustrate beautifully the courage and resilience displayed by DES-exposed men and women.

— *Louise Slaughter, U.S. Congresswoman*

DES Stories sheds new light on a public health tragedy. Author Margaret Braun, one of the first individuals to endure the adverse effects of this prescription drug, brings for the first time names and faces to DES. Her collection of stories provides healing for those exposed and serves as a critical reminder of the lives lost, and lives changed forever, due to an inadequately tested prescription drug.

— *Tom Harkin, U.S. Senator*

DES Stories

Faces and Voices of People Exposed to Diethylstilbestrol

By Margaret Lee Braun

Photographs by
Nancy M. Stuart

Foreword by
Theo Colborn, Ph.D.
co-author of *Our Stolen Future*
with Dianne Dumanoski and J. Peterson Myers

Visual Studies Workshop Press, Rochester, New York

Library of Congress Control Number
2001087228
Braun, Margaret Lee.
DES Stories: Faces and Voices of People Exposed to
Diethylstilbestrol
Margaret Lee Braun with photographs by Nancy M. Stuart
Includes 40 black-and-white photographs.
ISBN 0-89822-078-5
Visual Studies Workshop Press

Cover design by Geri McCormick
Book design by Geri McCormick
Edited by Ceil Goldman, David Pendergrass,
Deborah Fineblum Raub, Jonathan Sherwood

First Edition. Printed in the United States of America.
Visual Studies Workshop Press
Book and photo exhibit information:
DES Stories
P.O. Box 10114
Rochester, NY 14618
Web site: http://www.DESstories.com
Email: DESstories@aol.com

Disclaimer

This book intends to present a personal, social, and artistic re-
sponse to exposure to diethylstilbestrol. It is not the purpose of
this book to provide medical or legal information or advice. If
medical assistance is needed, you are urged to contact a medical
professional and/or national DES education organization for information pertaining to your concerns.

Every effort has been made to make this book as accurate as
possible. The stories in the book are reported anecdotally, by
persons exposed to DES and their families, and may not accu-
rately reflect all known information about DES. The book should
be used as an introduction to and not an ultimate source of information on DES exposure.

The author and Visual Studies Workshop Press shall have neither
liability nor responsibility to any person or entity with respect to
any error, loss, or damage caused, or alleged to be caused, directly or indirectly, by the information in this book.

If you do not wish to be bound by the above, you may return
this book to the publisher for a full refund.

To Charlotte J. Lee and Charles L. Braun, who are on every page of this book. — MLB

For David, Sarah, and Stuart. — NMS

Table of contents

DES (diethylstilbestrol)

DES was an undertested synthetic estrogen drug prescribed to millions of pregnant women. It was a profitable product, manufactured by over 200 pharmaceutical companies under more than 300 names.

DES was prescribed for over three decades, in the mistaken belief it could prevent miscarriage and enhance pregnancies. If you were born or were pregnant between 1938 and 1971, you could be exposed to DES.

There are an estimated ten million DES-exposed Americans, and hundreds of thousands of DES-exposed people around the world. Surveys report that DES has been used in 30 countries worldwide. In some European countries, DES was used well into the 1980s.

DES is linked to cancer and reproductive injuries in the daughters and sons exposed in utero, and in the mothers prescribed the drug. DES daughters have higher rates of vaginal and cervical cancer; increased incidence of reproductive problems, such as infertility, ectopic pregnancies, miscarriage, and premature delivery; and possible autoimmune problems. DES sons have a higher incidence of reproductive anomalies, including underdeveloped and undescended testicles, epididymal cysts, and structural changes. DES mothers have a higher incidence of breast cancer.

DES-exposed people are the largest population of people exposed, prenatally and inadvertently, to a synthetic estrogen, and DES injuries provide important scientific information. DES has become a significant model for how environmental estrogens may disrupt the reproductive systems of wildlife and humans.

All DES-exposed people need lifelong medical screening and to stay informed of potential health risks; researchers continue to identify consequences of DES exposure. Three questions stand out: How may DES affect other systems—endocrine, immune, cardiovascular, and skeletal? Will DES sons and daughters experience more health problems as they age? Will DES grandchildren suffer health problems from the DES prescribed to their grandmothers? One certainty remains: DES is a story in progress.

Foreword

Theo Colborn, Ph.D.

Fresh out of pharmacy college in 1947, I started filling DES prescriptions for pregnant women. By that time, it was considered medically correct, even stylish, to take DES just to have big, fat babies even though a woman was not threatened with miscarriage. DES was considered so safe that it was broadcast to chickens to produce capons; it was also fed to steers or implanted in their necks to speed up the production of beef on the hoof. Little did the physicians, or I and the other pharmacists dispensing DES at that time, understand the legacy of this course of treatment. Everyone was happy that this life-saving drug had been discovered, including the mothers who took DES. Five years after starting my pharmacy career, however, reports began circulating that perhaps DES was not as beneficial as had been touted and that it may actually increase miscarriages and premature births. But there were still physicians who continued to prescribe the medication.

It was not until 1971, when a *New England Journal of Medicine* article opened the Pandora's box of DES pharmacology, that the use of DES was discontinued during pregnancy. Quite by accident, Dr. Howard Ulfelder, a gynecologist, Dr. Arthur Herbst, an obstetrician, and Dr. David Poskanzer, an epidemiologist, all working at Massachusetts General Hospital, discovered that seven of eight young women diagnosed with a very rare, clear cell vaginal cancer had been exposed to DES via their mothers during the first three months of gestation. It did not take long before additional publications appeared in the scientific literature, gradually revealing the havoc DES had caused in the womb. Because the damage was invisible in many cases, and not expressed until the exposed individuals reached adulthood, it took time for the full impact of DES to be understood. Through the knowledge gained over the years, there is now no doubt that DES, a synthetic chemical, forever changed the destiny of the offspring who shared it with their mothers while in the womb. For them, federal intervention to restrict the use of DES was too late. This book tells the story of some of these individuals.

Reports began circulating that perhaps DES was not as beneficial as had been touted.

Today, a much larger global experiment is taking place with not one, but a number of synthetic chemicals that offspring and mothers are sharing through their blood before birth and the mothers' milk during breast feeding. To date, several hundred or more widely used contemporary industrial and agricultural chemicals have been shown to interfere with the natural chemical messengers that control development and function—as witnessed in wildlife, and proven in the laboratory. Just like DES, these chemicals in the environment interfere in a host of ways to disrupt the signals in the womb that tell the unborn how to develop according to the genes inherited from his or her mother and father. These synthetic chemicals have given us the wonders of plastic, the ability to feed the world, and made all things possible through electricity, to mention a few of the promises accompanying the products. They are an integral part of the world's commerce and, like DES, were designed to make our lives better. The story of DES provides a glimpse of what should be considered before we allow new chemicals to come on the market.

Never forget that DES has undermined the quality of life and potential of all of the people in this book. The costs to them and to society are unfathomable. The millions whose lives have been affected by DES should find some comfort from the fact that their story is serving as a harbinger of what can happen on a grand scale. It is a model of the chemical revolution's technological experiment—capable of changing the character of human societies and challenging the resilience of life on Earth. DES is a wake-up call to turn back the thoughtless dusting of the globe with untested chemicals to which most people do not know they are exposed.

DES Stories is only the first chapter of a much larger story. Anyone reading it will not want to see the DES story replayed in millions of individuals who will never know their lives were altered at the dictates of technology. Future generations are indebted to the author and those in this book for sharing their experience.

It took time for the full impact of DES to be understood.

Theo Colborn is senior program scientist and director of the Wildlife and Contaminants Project, World Wildlife Fund, USA. She is the co-author of Our Stolen Future *(Plume, 1997), with Dianne Dumanoski and J. Peterson Myers.*

Photographer's statement

Nancy M. Stuart

I always ask my students to define what a portrait is before beginning to explore the art and technique of making photographic portraits. The dictionary provides a limited answer: "a likeness of a person, especially one showing the face." If that were the case, our driver's license could suffice as a portrait. The goal in my own work, however, is to make portraits that go beyond this mere likeness to something more universal. This helps us comprehend human character through the photographic representation of an individual.

Photographer Richard Avedon once said, "A portrait is when the subject knows they are having their picture taken." This understatement captures an element of portraying people that I consider crucial because it assumes collaboration between the subject and the photographer. In *DES Stories* I depend on the openness and trust of people that I often meet just prior to the sitting. They are co-participants in the challenge of making the injuries of DES visible by giving a human face and story to something that cannot be seen. By looking into the camera, each participant in this project breaks through the anonymous wall around DES. They become healers and storytellers themselves.

Portraits are also about the person doing the portraying. In the course of producing the portraits for *DES Stories* I discovered a number of DES individuals among my friends and acquaintances. Daniel tells me of his sister's problems, not even aware that men may also be affected. Mary recalls how she was prescribed "something" during pregnancy. Her daughter has one healthy child after numerous miscarriages. I hear third hand about an old friend having serious complications from DES, the extent of which remains unspoken between us.

As I was flying to New York City to make more portraits for this series, I considered the commonalities I share with the participants in the project, though I am not DES-exposed myself. It is not necessary to experience the same attributes of each subject I photograph; what we share as human beings goes beyond the particular circumstances. I have great respect for the courage and dignity of people who are willing to share what has been invisible and private, until now.

By looking into the camera, each participant in this project breaks through the anonymous wall around DES. They become healers and storytellers themselves.

xi

The universe is made of stories,
not of atoms.

—Muriel Rukeyser

Introduction

Margaret Lee Braun

The seed for *DES Stories* was planted in 1971, when I was nineteen. I was recovering from DES-related cancer and I sent my doctor a handwritten note. "It seems to me," it said, "that women who are coping with this rare cancer could benefit from talking to each other." Dr. Herbst put me in touch with another young woman, hospitalized in Massachusetts. My new friend was 21 and full of interests. She wrote about studying Japanese, and where she'd like to travel. Suddenly she stopped writing. A month later she died. We never got far enough in our correspondence to talk about our feelings about DES, the cancer, or our own bodies.

The month I was operated on, the name DES was surfacing all over the media. It was declared a teratogen, meaning it causes birth defects, and was identified as the first transplacental carcinogen. It was linked to a rash of deaths and rare vaginal cancer in teenage girls. My surgeon, Arthur Herbst, had made medical history a few months earlier as one of the doctors who documented the link between clear cell cancer and DES. He told me I had cancer caused by a medicine prescribed to my mother during pregnancy. He said I was the 12th person in the country to be diagnosed.

I was too sick to care. Like a 19-year-old pulled off the battlefield, I woke up in a hospital bed forever changed. But, instead of losing my limbs, I had lost my organs, my functioning, my health—not to war, but to chemical exposure that had occurred 19 years in the past, before my own birth.

The same year, the FDA warned against the use of DES during pregnancy. But by then nearly five million pregnant women in the United States and hundreds of thousands more around the world had taken the drug, assured by their doctors that it would enable them to give birth to healthy babies. In some countries, doctors continued prescribing DES during pregnancy into the 1980s. Despite evidence of dangers, DES remained a popular and profitable product for decades, used in over 100 treatments. It was distributed on college campuses as the morning-after pill, given to women after pregnancy to suppress lactation, and used as a growth stimulator to add weight to livestock.

As the news about DES emerged, my family struggled to grasp what had happened. It seemed beyond imagining that a pill, taken before I even existed, could devastate my body years later. We did not quite realize that our private catastrophe was a public issue. But DES was like a tidal wave that had begun thirty years earlier. And it was beginning to break against the baby boom generation.

Eventually, the World Health Organization, the National Cancer Institute, hundreds of scientific articles, and leading medical school textbooks would define DES as a potent carcinogen and the cause of reproductive injuries for millions. Yet pharmaceutical companies would continue to deny that DES caused adverse effects.

Finding each other

After recovering enough to be able to walk and sit, I tried a class at the local university. As I sat in the classroom full of 20-year-olds, I struggled to compose myself outwardly, to hide my physical pain. I felt like a girl from another planet, or someone who'd returned from war—the DES wars. I wanted desperately to understand what had happened to me, but I found that the people I trusted to tell about DES and cancer were few. Another DES daughter once told me, "DES is something that happens to you in private, in the middle of the night." It was in these hard times, with the help of loving friends and family, that my DES wounds began to heal.

It took a full nine years after my cancer treatment for me to meet, for the first time, another woman who had had DES cancer. Susan Helmrich exuded friendly energy, the kind that draws people out. Soon we were sharing stories of learning that we were DES-exposed, and of the day each of us found out we had cancer.

I told Susan how I had begun to search for other cancer survivors. We agreed that women shouldn't have to deal with the devastating losses of clear cell cancer on their own. Susan knew Joyce Bichler, a DES cancer survivor who had written about her experience in her book, *DES Daughter*, and who had a similar instinct to reach out to others. Working with DES Action, a pioneering consumer group founded by DES mothers, the three of us established the DES Cancer Network. It was an impulse both practical and defiant. We wanted to get information out. And we wanted to break through the wall of anonymity and silence. DES is a public health catastrophe, not a private shame. Why should DES cancer survivors not know each another? We would find one another, and find out who we were.

The idea of toxic exposure before birth resulting in life-threatening injuries years later sounded like a science fiction novel.

DES was a charged issue in the medical community. The link between DES and clear cell cancer was controversial. Clear cell cancer records at the University of Chicago had been subpoenaed by one of the drug companies looking for loopholes in the research. There were doctors all over the country, still in practice, who had prescribed DES for years; some were sensitive about being blamed or possibly sued. And, though the best physicians contacted their patients, others did not. Many mothers searching for their medical records were told that a flood or fire had destroyed the files. Unfortunately, this meant hundreds of thousands of people were left in the dark about DES. Nevertheless, a number of concerned oncologists made our names available to their patients. We found each other, one by one, through these oncologists, DES Action, the media, and word of mouth.

The rarity of the cancer, and the geographic dispersion of DES cancer daughters, made finding other women like looking for needles in a haystack. It was tough work; we had only a few hundred dollars to make ourselves known. In addition, I barely had the confidence to talk about DES. The idea of toxic exposure before birth resulting in life-threatening injuries years later sounded like a science fiction novel. Love Canal, Agent Orange, and asbestos were just entering public consciousness; a chemical that hurt people, like DES, had never been heard of before.

The DES Cancer Network

In meeting DES survivors, my sense of the trauma of DES was confirmed. I met women who had nightmares, reliving the medical treatment they'd undergone. I met men reluctant to admit they were exposed to DES. I met mothers whose eyes spilled with tears when they talked about how they thought they had been doing the right thing by taking DES. And, over and over, people told me they had never told their story to anyone. It was clear that putting people in touch with others offered healing that medicine could not.

DES daughters at all stages of recovery began to turn to the DES Cancer Network with fundamental concerns. How many of us are alive? What are my chances of getting a recurrence? What kind of surgery should I have? Bombarded with life-and-death questions, we started researching and writing educational materials.

Slowly, the DES Cancer Network grew. I was the volunteer coordinator managing the organization from my home office in Rochester, N.Y. Susan was in graduate school in Boston studying epidemiology. With a core of committed members, we took calls from around the country, recording medical histories, referring to oncologists, and linking people to one other. Like stones tossed into the water, our ripples of influence grew wider and wider.

Building the DES Cancer Network began to take most of my time. I quit my job as a movement therapist and became its full-time director. The suffering caused by DES electrified me—but there were times I'd put the phone down and put my head in my hands, not sure I was up to the enormity of the DES disaster. My own health was still shaky. Yet somehow I knew that as much as I was helping others, I was being healed as well. Most of all, I sensed that people needed to tell their stories; they needed to know their stories mattered. I began to realize how important community acknowledgement is for healing.

The work closest to my heart was our annual conference, held in a different city each year. Here women could share the trauma of DES cancer and help each other move on. In our healing circle, each person had a chance to tell her story. Bound together by common experience, we sat in awe, as much at what our bodies had endured as our accomplishments: journalist, singer, law student, pilot, art teacher, mother, marathon runner. We brought in speakers: oncologists, psychologists, and lawyers. We made art, performed healing rituals and put on skits that poked fun at every aspect of our collective pain: vaginas, bladders, and gynecologists. We coached newly diagnosed patients, helped people recover, and celebrated new loves and adoptions. Eventually, our database of clear cell cancer cases became the largest record outside of the medical profession, and the network became a national educational organization with members in more than 40 states and several countries.

Getting the word out

But as we educated each other through the DES Cancer Network, the dearth of information on DES became scarier. By the early '90s, more women with recurrences were showing up at our annual meetings, desperate for information. There were no established offices in government or medicine to oversee DES concerns. The registry maintained at the University of Chicago to track clear cell cancer had lost its funding. When we turned to the medical literature, there was no documentation of recurrence of clear cell cancer. Our Network, made up of cancer survivors— and DES Action—had the closest finger on the pulse. I lay awake at night terrified *we might be the only ones who know.*

DES injuries were bad enough. The pharmaceutical industry's refusal to acknowledge or assist victims was another layer of wrongdoing. But the fact that DES daughters were dying, and no one knew about it, really motivated us.

It was wrenching for me to see my friends die from clear cell cancer. There were too many good-byes knowing it would be the last time we would talk. When a member of our board, Karin, died at 28, I flew to Wisconsin for her service, full of grief. Karin and I had become good friends and as she grew closer to her death, we talked for hours on the phone. Whenever my energy flagged, I could hear her soft, passionate voice exhorting me to continue the fight to bring attention to DES.

By this time, Susan was an epidemiologist working at Boston University. We decided to conduct a pilot study of the survival rates of our members. Data in hand, we flew to the University of Chicago to present it to Arthur Herbst. Our reunion began a collaboration with Dr. Herbst, whom I had not seen in ten years, and his administrator, Diane Anderson. Dr. Herbst told us that if we could find funding, he would commit to saving the clear cell cancer registry.

Epidemiologists at Boston University agreed to help us carry out a more formal study of our membership, to be presented at scientific conferences. The same year the work of DES Action, and a DES daughter's play about DES, were drawing attention to the DES research crisis. When I presented a paper calling for DES research, at a National Institutes of Health hearing on women's health, my paper was circulated throughout the NIH and I was filmed for a PBS documentary on DES, *Health Quarterly*.

One day, in my hometown of Rochester, I met up with long-time friend, N.Y. Congresswoman Louise Slaughter. I had worked with her on the campaign to update the New York statute of limitations, so victims of toxic exposure could seek justice in court. Slaughter's knowledge of DES and her background in public health gave her a keen grasp of the DES situation. Without hesitation, she invited me to Washington, where she arranged meetings with legislators. With representatives from DES Action and the DES Cancer Network, we began to make the rounds on Capitol Hill. We met legislators and staff personally touched by DES, but who never thought to mention it, because it never came up. A senator from the Midwest shared the pain of his wife's DES-triggered, repeated miscarriages. A congressional intern recalled that his two sisters were exposed to DES. It seemed wherever we mentioned DES, we found someone who was DES-exposed or knew a neighbor or relative who was.

The fact that DES daughters were dying, and no one knew about it, really motivated us.

Recognition

In the summer of 1991 I wrote to Samuel Broder, M.D., then director of the National Cancer Institute. I proposed a meeting regarding DES research, and to my surprise he agreed. The following month, Nora Cody, executive director of DES Action, and I flew to Washington to meet with Dr. Broder and his division chiefs.

There I began to talk about what DES exposure is like for young women and men, and the burden of guilt that DES mothers carry. Nora talked about animal studies that show DES could affect the immune system, and how no one knows what lies ahead. Dr. Broder listened keenly; after the meeting, many of the scientists stayed to talk.

Dr. Broder turned out to be a compassionate crusader. Within months he convened the first-ever scientific conference on DES. What was remarkable was that it brought together the entire cast of the DES universe: People who had been hurt by DES, consumer groups, doctors and researchers whose dedication to DES had built their careers, women's health leaders, lawyers, and policy makers. Talks were presented, recommendations made, and the highest scientific body in the country, the NIH, conferred the ultimate scientific stamp of approval—that research on the long-term effects of DES exposure is "scientifically appropriate." Finally, DES had status.

With renewed interest in DES in Washington, the press picked up on the issue. Women and men from DES Action and the DES Cancer Network began to go public with their stories to win support for the DES bill—even though talking about personal injuries was the hardest thing to do. We appeared on and in *Good Morning America, CNN, The Los Angeles Times, USA Today, The Washington Post*, and more than 20 major newspapers nationwide. With Congresswoman Slaughter, we co-authored a federal bill for DES research and education. She introduced the bill to Congress, followed by Iowa Senator Tom Harkin's lead in the Senate. Letters and calls descended on Washington, describing reproductive damage, illness, death, lost pregnancies, heartbreak, fears, and outrage.

It seemed wherever we mentioned DES, we found someone who was DES-exposed or knew a neighbor or relative who was.

In late 1992, the DES Research and Education Amendment was signed into law by President George Bush. Washington veterans said it was astounding for a bill to pass in less than a year. It was thrilling, but I couldn't forget that it had been 21 years since the link between DES and cancer came to light.

Since then, the clear cell cancer registry has been revived. In addition, DES studies around the country have been updated and merged into one large program under the NCI, called the DES Combined Cohort Studies (DCCS). As a result, several studies tracking the health of DES-exposed people are now yielding important information. DES legislation has passed for the second time, and a national education program is being carried out by the Center for Disease Control. But more recently, getting the dollars has been an uphill battle—a reminder that DES legislation and follow-up of the DES population are not guaranteed.

Most of all, I like to remember that underlying the public awareness of DES are people, telling their stories. By sharing their stories, in personal and public communities, they have made DES better understood and less shrouded in silence. And in telling their stories, people have changed themselves, and changed the way the world responds.

Preface

Margaret Lee Braun

I started out searching for DES stories because I wanted to find my own story in others' experience. I wanted to better understand what had happened to me, and how to feel about it. Over the years, as I talked with hundreds of DES-exposed people, I found myself increasingly compelled to record people's stories. I am moved by what people have overcome, by their thoughts about it, and the passion of their feeling, often thinking, "Somebody should hear this. This is incredible!"

I began to see that DES happens one person at a time, and every DES-exposed person has an important story to tell. These are stories of personal and collective healing. They also reveal, in heartbreaking clarity, the consequences of our chemical age. In every corner of our planet, scientists are observing reproductive dysfunction in animals and humans that are similar to the injuries seen in DES offspring. It turns out that DES is one of many environmental exposures disrupting our balance of life.

As these stories illustrate, beyond a shadow of a doubt, the effects of DES are more than a litany of consequences, "structural and cellular reproductive changes in the offspring of women prescribed DES." DES touches the body and soul. The efforts it takes some DES daughters to have a healthy baby are painfully real — the deep, daily worry over reproduction, a process that in the ordinary scheme of things is part of the ebb and flow of life — do not appear in any medical paper. Neither does the impact of DES on sexual identity show up on a list of DES effects, or the costs of tests and treatments, or the children and grandchildren who will never be, or a hundred other examples of the way DES shapes people's lives. Personal stories are at the heart of the DES experience and cry out for documentation. The more we tell our stories, the more we heal, and the greater our power to spread knowledge, understanding, and hope.

Listening to the stories of DES-exposed men and women, I have felt full of thousands of stories, stories in search of a voice to speak — and I have felt a responsibility to pass them along. It is my way of bearing witness. I particularly want to share the faces of people, to show the human side of DES.

In this mission, I found a skilled and sensitive collaborator in photographer Nancy Stuart. Nancy and I traveled around the country, meeting and photographing individuals and their families. In interviewing over 60 people for *DES Stories*, I asked each participant, "What has happened to you because of DES?" and "What does being DES-exposed mean to you?" My intention all along is to allow people to speak from the heart, so the stories of DES are not lost.

The stories in these pages are gathered from women and men exposed to DES between 1948–1971 in 19 U.S. states and three countries. Thirty-seven of the participants were exposed in utero or prescribed DES during pregnancy. Three of the inter-

> *The more we tell our stories, the more we heal, and the greater our power to spread knowledge.*

views were conducted with a DES father, a DES husband, and a DES granddaughter. The stories represent a range of DES consequences, and a range of feelings about being DES-exposed; they do not intend to be a statistical cross-section of the DES population. The responses reflect individuals' attitudes and knowledge at a point in time. Some people are familiar with DES research and medical terminology; others tell their stories without using a single medical term. By contributing to a public dialogue about DES, the people in *DES Stories* are themselves becoming more educated, and freeing others to talk about DES as well.

As I interviewed people for *DES Stories*, I began to notice a common theme. We are not always sure how to feel about DES. As survivors, are we lucky or not lucky? Should we be angry or sad? How does DES figure in the scheme of things?

One woman told me she is always on the lookout for something written about DES, because there is so little. "It's not a topic that comes up," she said; "it's not something you talk about at a party, or point to and say, 'This is where I got hurt.'"

In fact, the silence around DES is oddly disproportionate to its widespread impact. We're taught to know something is important if it has a voice and presence in the culture. In the case of DES, the *absence* of voice reveals the impact of DES. In the same way that DES wounds are hard to point to, there's a parallel beneath-the-surface reality—the impact on people's lives.

I am moved by people's spirit in sharing the personal stories that make up the *DES Stories* book and exhibit. Not everyone I invited to participate in the project accepted. The wounds of DES can be too personal or too sexual to talk about; others don't want to cause their mothers any more pain. Everyone has their own way of dealing, and healing.

A comment from one man in his early '40s, who first talked openly about his DES injuries, is representative of many more: "I'm glad to share my thoughts but I have a professional life. I'm not interested in the world knowing my intimate story and I won't have my photograph in a book. But it *is* important for DES sons to come forward."

After hearing hundreds of stories of suffering, I know that DES is a story of violation. Yet it is also a story of healing and triumph. Most people I speak with feel outrage about DES, but refuse to be victimized by it.

Many say their DES experience is a double-edged sword of catastrophe and strength.

Many say their DES experience is a double-edged sword of catastrophe and strength. People tell me they value their lives and live their lives more fully, because of the hardships they've suffered from DES. They take better care of themselves and treasure the precious gift of health. They are more appreciative of their blessings, including the children and young people in their life, because of what has been threatened or lost because of DES.

People exposed to DES have shown incredible determination in building families and careers while juggling stresses of medical exams, treatments, chronic illness, and adoption or surrogacy. I know many people who have made career choices to become health professionals, lawyers, teachers, spiritual mentors, and artists, directly because of what they encountered. They are putting their experience to use, to make something positive out of the injustice of DES.

DES provides so many important lessons: about prenatal estrogen exposure; the fragility of the fetus; the testing and marketing of pharmaceuticals; and the link between reproductive injuries and environmental contaminants. But behind the science on DES lie the lives of people who are living the experience of DES exposure and have a message to share. My wish is that these stories will communicate the emotional impact of DES exposure, and indicate how environmental contaminants may affect the most personal aspects of people's lives.

Those of us who have had to incorporate the fact of DES into our being, and observe how it has played out for ourselves and hundreds of thousands of others, have also had to figure out how to express the fact of it. Like canaries in the coal mine, we are the messengers—the ones who have lived the story. And, each of us must find our own meaning. It will never be possible to gather every story or measure the cumulative toll of DES. But my hope is that the DES experience might return, in wisdom and strength, what it has cost.

Behind the science on DES lie the lives of people who are living the experience of DES exposure and have a message to share.

Through the experience of DES, we realize the interconnectedness of life; how we are linked with all populations, human and wildlife, who are vulnerable to chemical contamination. The idea that choices we make today may affect the quality of life decades into the future is not an intellectual concept for DES-exposed people; it is knowledge that imbues their stories with veracity and urgency. We know that we share a fragility with all life, as well as an extraordinary potential to heal.

Here, then, are people searching for ways to communicate the experience of DES. Ultimately, showing our faces and sharing our stories is a way to make DES visible, as we take DES from out of the shadows by speaking from the heart. For if DES-exposed people don't tell the stories of DES, who will?

Faces and Voices

I carried around the film of my uterus for some time.

I'd been going from one doctor to another to find out why I hadn't had my period for almost a year. When the lab technician saw my uterus, he did a double take and said, "Um, do you mind if I put a little bit more dye in you?" I was told that my uterus was just too small, that it was deformed and probably couldn't carry a baby to term.

One doctor said that if there were any chance I could bear a child, I would have to be in bed, on my back, for the entire duration of the pregnancy. My husband and I had a fertility workup, and when the doctor came back he announced, "Brad, you are a sexual superman. Alice, you were born to write plays."

I carried around the film of my uterus for some time, and I would bring it with me to doctors' offices and say, "Here's the 8 x 10 glossy of my deformed uterus, doctor." And the doctors would look at it and say, "Doesn't look good."

My mother took DES, as everyone did, with great faith and a sense of responsibility to her unborn child. Not only was DES ineffective, but her risk of breast cancer was increased. She went through hell with a debilitating double mastectomy before she died at the age of 57. And there is no history of breast cancer in my family.

DES has changed my whole identity in terms of health and well-being. I look fine, but I have invisible birth defects.

—Alice Cohen

Alice discovered, at the age of 18, that she had been exposed to DES in utero. She was later diagnosed with DES-related cellular changes, an unusually small and deformed uterus, hormonal imbalance, and infertility. Alice and her husband adopted their daughter four years ago.

Alice writes for television and the stage. Her play *Philomela's Tapestry* uses a Greek myth to communicate the DES story. The myth tells the story of Philomela, who is raped. She vows to tell what has happened, but her assailant cuts out her tongue. Silenced and wounded, she finds another way to speak—by weaving her story into a tapestry to show to the world.

DES daughter Alice Cohen

Exposed 1954

I had gone as far as I was willing with infertility treatments.

I was in vet school when I first heard about DES. The professor pointed at a diagram of a chemical and called it diethylstilbestrol. He talked about how it was put in chickens and fed to cattle to make them grow faster—until it started causing the workers in the slaughterhouses to grow breasts, and they stopped using it.

It was around then that I found out I was exposed to DES. My older sister had a miscarriage, and we learned it was because she was DES-exposed. My mom took DES with both my sisters and me because in those days that particular doctor gave everybody DES.

At one point I was taking Clomid and Pergonal to stimulate ovulation for the in vitro fertilization treatments. I gained 50 pounds and felt nauseated around the clock. I remember thinking, "Who knows what these fertility drugs are doing? I don't want to do this any more."

I had gone as far as I was willing with infertility treatments. I remember thinking specifically, "If I am going through all this because my mother took DES, what am I exposing a potential baby of mine to?" It was a relief when our first adoption came through. My mother didn't know that the DES she took would have lasting effects on her children. There wasn't anything I could do about that now, except not to expose another fetus to something that might be the next disaster.

In the long run the only thing DES means to me is that my kids are adopted. I never think about it on a daily basis. And I'm very happy with the way my family's turned out.

—Patti Sislen

Patti's mother was given DES when pregnant with each of her three daughters. Patti's older sister suffered DES-related miscarriages and went on to adopt two children. Patti, who was diagnosed with a DES-caused malformed uterus, lost her first pregnancy to a miscarriage. Her next two pregnancies were ectopic and required diagnostic and reconstructive surgeries. Years of debilitating infertility treatments followed. Finally, Patti chose to stop the treatment, and she and her husband began adoption research. They adopted son Everett from Vietnam and son Mark from Korea. Soon after this photo, the family adopted a daughter from Korea.

DES daughter Patti Sislen, with sons, Everett and Mark

Exposed 1951

Lately, I've been actually telling people that I'm DES-exposed.

Cryosurgery was the first thing I had. It's a freezing of part of the cervix. They put something like a dry ice up you, a gas. And it's very uncomfortable, very heavy cramping, and it's supposed to freeze these cells and get rid of them. But that didn't work. The cells were too high up. My doctor was going to do a conization next, and remove a slice of the cervix, but he said there was a chance that bleeding from it would lead to hysterectomy.

It was like leading a dual life—trying to hold down a full-time job, going through DES procedures, and having surgeries.

The boss would be mad because I'd have to take personal time, or I'd be late coming back from a treatment. If the treatment didn't work, I'd be devastated. One time I had complications after laser surgery, a lot of pain and bleeding, and I had to take a whole week off. I didn't like having to tell my boss personal things.

If DES were something that showed on your arm or your leg, then I could talk about it. But it's such a private subject.

Lately, I've been actually telling people that I'm DES-exposed. I think it needs to be said. It's time for me to make people aware of what has happened, and to what could happen. Maybe somebody listening will ask their mother, and their mother will say, "Gee, I don't know," and check and find out. Because it's so important that people know. For good or bad, they need to know.

—Aimee Gasparre

Like many other women, Aimee's mother, Ruth, thought she'd taken only vitamins during her pregnancy. Years later she discovered that DES had been prescribed in combination with the vitamins. Doctors told Aimee that she had classic signs of DES exposure: a shortened cervix; a T-shaped uterus, identified through a surgical laparoscopy; and dysplasia, or abnormal cell growth on the cervix, which required cryosurgery —a procedure no longer recommended for DES daughters. After four years of trying to conceive, Aimee and her husband adopted their infant daughter, Alexandra, from Guatemala.

Aimee is a marketing assistant in the manufacturing industry.

DES daughter Aimee Gasparre, with mother, Ruth Peck

Exposed 1956

I was a child having my future cut out of me.

At the time I was diagnosed with DES-related cancer, I was still a child; I didn't know anything about being a woman. It was my first pelvic exam. They knew right away that there was something very wrong. The specialist said, "We think your mother took this strange drug DES." My mother remembered taking it and could describe the color of the pill.

I was a child having my future cut out of me, and my womanhood. I had a complete radical hysterectomy. It wasn't just the regular hysterectomy that lots of people have, "garden variety."

For me sex is painful. I have bladder and continency problems because of all the surgery, and I will use catheters for the rest of my life. That's hard to say. To think that somebody else will know that.

I've had to face up to the fact that this happened to me. I've had to recognize that there are things that have been taken from me that I still mourn for. But I've gone on with my life not totally victimized. For me it's the difference between being wounded and being victimized. It's all been little steps. Two steps forward and one step back.

Each time I make a new friend or talk more easily to someone on the phone, each time I sing a song with the kind of feeling where I don't hold back—each day these little things happen, I'm getting past it more and more.

—Susan Simpson

Susan was diagnosed with DES-related vaginal cancer at the age of 19. She underwent a radical hysterectomy, vaginectomy, and reconstructive surgery. As a result of her cancer treatment, Susan suffers from a neurogenic bladder, a chronic condition involving loss of bladder sensation.

Susan, an accountant, has pursued her love of singing to become a concert vocalist.

DES daughter Susan Simpson

Exposed 1956

Each of us has to live with her own ghosts.

I hadn't spoken to my obstetrician in 25 years. I tracked him down because I wanted to find out what type of DES I had been given. When I told him that Nina had been diagnosed with DES cancer, he put the phone down and cried.

What bothers me most is that you always want your child to have what you had, plus. To think that what I did prevents Nina from having the kind of relationship that I have with her—to me that's the big loss. I've somehow denied her the pleasure I've had in having her.

How do DES mothers cope with their feelings? The kind of guilt I feel is a great sadness. But it's not the same as the guilt from doing something I knew was wrong. We did what the doctors told us was best for the pregnancy. It doesn't change the grief, though. It's like making a wrong turn and having a car accident. Each of us has to live with her own ghosts.

My eyes have been really opened by DES. I'm in the construction business and I don't see any difference between drug companies putting drugs out before they are properly tested and a road builder who doesn't put down the right foundation and later someone gets killed.

I mean, in many ways our suffering is not that different from families who suffer from any kind of tragedy. The only thing that does distinguish DES is that it need not have happened.

—Judy Weisman

When Judy Weisman was 28, she was overjoyed to learn she was pregnant. Judy's obstetrician told her everything was fine, but he prescribed DES "to prevent that 1 in 400 chance of miscarriage." Nina was born nine months later.

Twenty-eight years later, at the same age her mother took DES, Nina developed the rare vaginal cancer linked to DES exposure. She underwent a radical hysterectomy, vaginectomy, and lymphadenectomy to save her life. A vaginal reconstruction, using a skin graft from Nina's thigh, was done to create a neovagina. After the surgery, she received extensive radiation.

Nina survived DES-related cancer but has painful secondary medical problems. She loves the outdoors and works as a park ranger in the Sierra Mountains. Judy is a business manager in the construction industry.

DES mother Judy Weisman, with daughter, Nina Weisman

Exposed 1963

They really thought they could improve on nature.

I've never had any problems from DES. I feel like there must be some abnormality from my exposure, but I haven't figured out what. I'm either a natural optimist or a denier. You never know about testicular cancer; it enters my mind. I would be happy to know more about the effects on men.

I've thought about DES. Here's a generation exposed to an agent given with no knowledge of the effects. What strikes me is the naive, blind faith that some foreign substance would improve on nature. Yet, this was a generation with a very different perspective on chemicals. This is the generation that conquered TB, that developed penicillin.

It's much more complicated than "those are the villains." The scientists of the 1940s and 1950s were coming up with drugs that treated what was never before treatable. They felt they could accomplish everything they set their minds to. They had within their grasp the conquest of tuberculosis and the control of polio—as well as the eradication of smallpox and malaria.

This was a generation that had beaten Hitler's armies and developed the atomic bomb. They had tremendous belief that science and technology, pharmacology, and chemistry could solve the world's problems and not create a mess. They really thought they could improve on nature.

It was a heady time. Arrogance came out of real accomplishment, not thin air. But along with accomplishment was this incredible shortsightedness. I don't know if the two can be divorced. Certainly, it is not a perfect world.

—David Mock

David's parents told him he was DES-exposed soon after learning about the adverse effects of DES on daughters. David's mother tried to find research on DES and sons but could locate very little information. Like millions of women, she was prescribed DES because a prior pregnancy had ended in a miscarriage. She took DES every day during her pregnancy, beginning in the second week.

Like many DES sons and daughters, David has experienced no health problems he can attribute to DES. Married with three children, he is a doctor specializing in infectious disease.

DES son David Mock

Exposed 1950

You don't ever get over it. Never.

In my generation you had your kids fast. I had my eldest son when I was twenty. When I got pregnant again, I went to the doctor. He said, "Take this before you have any problems." And he gave me a prescription for DES. So I took it, not needing it. When the druggist handed me the DES he said, "This is made by a great company and it is a wonder drug."

Susan was born in 1951. She was the only girl in our family. And she was doted on. She was in the gifted program in school and had lots of friends. There were sleep-over parties, sports, school, all the usual.

One day, when she was 16, she called to me from her bedroom: "Ma, come in, I want to show you something." There was a growth coming from her vagina. The doctors were stunned. They had absolutely no idea what it could be. Then they discovered it was malignant. We couldn't find any doctors in America—I'm talking about the whole of America—that knew anything.

Sue suffered terribly those years. She was in and out of the hospital while trying to graduate from high school. She went through operation upon operation upon operation.

First the cancer and her uterus were removed. Then they decided that they'd better remove all the organs, including the vagina. So that was another operation. I would work, run into the city, sit with her. One day she turned to me and said, "Why didn't you tell me I had no time?"

It's many years and I still find it very hard to talk about my daughter's death. You don't ever get over it. Never. When the studies starting coming out I wouldn't discuss it. I just could not speak about it.

—Helen Greene

Helen was prescribed DES "just to make sure" that she wouldn't have any problems. Months later she gave birth to her second child and only daughter, Susan. Susan developed into a talented student with a love of acting. At the age of 16 Susan was diagnosed with vaginal clear cell cancer, which spread to her lungs and liver. She died in her parents' arms at the age of 17. The Greenes did not learn until several years after Susan's death that her cancer was caused by the DES she had been exposed to in utero.

DES mother Helen Greene and husband, Al Greene, with photograph of their deceased daughter, Susan Greene

Exposed 1950

It's pretty beat.
That's a light term for something really painful.

I've been through ten miscarriages. It messed with me to the point the doctor asked if I wanted to make it so I wouldn't get pregnant. It's pretty beat. That's a light term for something really painful.

My dad loves children. He and my mom are extremely saddened that they don't have grandchildren. The last time I miscarried, I told my dad. He looked down and shook his head real slowly and said, "Geez."

The time I was pregnant the longest, my mom took me to a restaurant by the lake and was very excited. "Have some soup. Have some salad." She talked about what room the baby would stay in, and told me she'd watch the baby when I went back to work.

It's getting to the point where you feel you might as well have a drink with dinner. You go through the prenatal, you don't lift anything, you eat the right food. What the hell's the use? It's like,

"Damn it, I don't want to go through this again." I don't go for the initial visit with the gynecologist. Now if I'm pregnant, I keep it to myself.

What hurts is my husband and I don't talk much about this any more. The emotions just sit there.

The women at work are constantly having baby showers. You see these little itty bitty babies and you know they can be stinky and noisy but you just want to hold them and nibble them and love them. The thought that I may never be sitting there, holding up the booties, really gets to me. For a while I'd pop in, give a gift, and leave. Now I send a gift and don't go.

Nothing a lawyer could get me for DES can replace these human needs that outweigh the financial needs. Mom told me she'd pay for in vitro fertilization—even if it cost $10,000, she'll foot the bill. But it wouldn't help anyway. It doesn't seem like anything can make up for it.

—Pam Crist

Pam shared her story after her mom sent her a newspaper article about the *DES Stories* project. Although her mother sends Pam articles on DES whenever she sees one, they don't talk much about DES face to face.

Pam had her first gynecologic exam before she had her period, at age 12. Her mom explained to her, "A lot of people born under this medicine need this checkup because you are at risk for cancer."

Pam has been married for nine years. She has had ten miscarriages and no successful pregnancies. She and her husband have had chromosome testing and other infertility workups and Pam has undergone several D&Cs.

After a hysterosalpingogram medical procedure, in which dye is injected into the uterus to show its shape in an ultrasound, Pam learned her uterus is misshapen from DES.

Pam works as service representative at a federal credit union.

DES daughter Pam Crist, with her parents, Walter and Phila Eves

Exposed 1961

For most people, having children is something that happens.

For most people, having children is something that happens. You decide that you want children and it's only a piece of life. But I had to stop and make it my whole life to make it happen.

The roughest part was the expectations. We lived from month to month. I would get very hopeful. Getting pregnant and being a mother was my life's dream. Since I was in high school and met my husband, all I ever wanted to do was marry him and have his children.

When I began to realize I was DES-exposed, I became really angry that my husband and I hadn't known about the DES exposure so we could have started the adoption process sooner. I'm sure we'll adopt two children; maybe we can squeeze in three. But I spent so many years denying myself this.

Alexandra is a miracle in our life. It's sort of confusing, because before her I had strong feelings of being incapacitated and infertile and having my whole life influenced by the drug companies. Now we have Alexandra and we feel like she is meant for us and we were meant for her. If it hadn't been for DES, I would never have known Alexandra. And I'm so thankful! She's just absolutely the perfect child for us and we never would have conceived her.

What's most ironic is that the birth mother is from Indianapolis. When we learned that Alexandra was up for adoption we drove there. As we exited from the highway, we couldn't believe it; looming before us was the huge international headquarters of Eli Lilly, the largest manufacturer of DES. We pulled off to the side of the road and sat silently, looking. We didn't know whether to laugh or cry.

—Gaylene Fraser

Since the age of 14, Gaylene has experienced irregular bleeding and severe pain every month during menstruation. When she was in her late twenties, a doctor diagnosed her as having a T-shaped uterus and a cervical hood, or extra structure, around the opening of the cervix. At first Gaylene's mother did not remember having taken DES, but with Gaylene's encouragement she was able to locate the medical records and confirm that she was prescribed DES during her pregnancy.

Gaylene and her husband tried to conceive for 12 years. Gaylene took the hormone Pergonal for many years to induce ovulation. She tried artificial insemination, then suffered an ectopic pregnancy and underwent emergency hospitalization. Eventually Gaylene and Rob adopted Alexandra, followed by a son. Gaylene is a full-time mother and school volunteer.

DES daughter Gaylene Fraser with husband, Rob, and daughter, Alexandra

Exposed 1951

DES *is not only in Holland.*
DES *is all over the world.*

Why do I tell my story? Because DES is not only me. DES is not only in Holland. DES is all over the world.

I was pregnant twice and miscarried. I thought, "It must be Mother Nature." Then I started to search the Internet for DES, and bang, I had the realization, "This is not Mother Nature. This is the medicine my mother took."

When I got pregnant for the third time, it turned out to be ectopic. The embryo was growing in the fallopian tube instead of the uterus. I was rushed to the hospital. It almost cost me my life. The fallopian tube ruptured and there was free spill of blood in the abdomen. I was devastated by the loss of the fetus, but I was glad to be alive.

I got pregnant again eight months ago. It was the fourth time in 12 years. We were so ex-cited. This time we could see the heartbeat on the ultrasound. But the embryo lodged in the fallopian tube again. I could see my baby— just a few centimeters away from the uterus. That's how close to having a baby!

They had to remove my fallopian tube and the embryo. I was in denial at the time and even joked, "Can't they just put a zipper in my tummy? That would be handy for the next ectopic."

Then I got mad. "I'm going to fight this DES thing." But what to fight? Who to fight? Then comes the loss, the despair. Why don't we get a baby? Why do I get pregnant, only to have it taken away?

My husband, Jos, and I still hope. We believe it will happen the natural way. If not, we'll consider adoption, or in vitro fertilization, or

—story continued on page 22

DES daughter Marjon Floris

Exposed 1964

Marjon was born in northeast Holland. She is one of an estimated 440,000 Dutch exposed to DES in The Netherlands.

Marjon's mother was pre-scribed DES starting in the 11th week of pregnancy. Records show she took DES before and after Marjon's birth. Marjon's two older sisters are also DES-exposed. They suffered years of pregnancy prob-lems, but eventually were able to have children.

Marjon has had difficulty becoming pregnant. Over 12 years, she has had four pregnancies, with two miscarriages and two ectopic pregnancies, resulting in emergency surgeries, the loss of embryos, and the loss of a fallopian tube. Marjon has been told her uterus is small due to DES exposure.

Marjon is a freelance photographer. She keeps informed through DES Center The Nether-lands, an organization that carries out DES education and advocacy in Europe.

DES *daughter Marjon Floris (continued)*

just letting go. We can be happy without children, but having just one would be the icing on the cake.

I don't tell my story to be pitiful. I want to let people know that a chemical has done harm to people all over the world. Chemicals are advertised as if we can't live without them. Pesticides, solvents, food additives, contaminants. What are we doing?

DES people need to be heard. We need to make it known to the world what has happened to us. The Dutch have a saying, "Shared grief is half the grief." By telling our stories together, in the open, the feeling that we are never alone in this will make our emotional wounds start to heal. Even people who are not able to talk about DES—when they hear another person's story, it reveals a secret in themselves they've kept for so long—and they will feel relieved.

—Marjon Floris

*I*t is difficult to call to mind any subject upon which more rubbish has been written than the sex hormones. This is very largely the result of the general public's desire for the maintenance of youth and all that it implies, together with the successful exploitation of this trait by commercial firms.

—*E. Charles Dodds, M.D.*
Synthesizer of DES

They need to see the human side to this.

My husband, who was an obstetrician, evidently knew what caused Pennie's cancer but chose to keep it from me. We took Pennie to a cancer specialist in Indianapolis. Her dad kind of broke down; he was so scared she wasn't going to make it. So instead of having him for a rock, I had to be the rock, and that was the only time that ever happened in our lives.

I really don't know why he didn't tell me about DES. I found out by reading Good Housekeeping. There was an article that said this medicine, DES, caused the kind of cancer that Pennie had. It was the name of the drug that struck a chord with me. When I told Pennie what I learned in the magazine, she said her dad had already told her.

What gets me more than anything is why something didn't happen to me and not to my daughter. I was the one that took the medicine and it isn't right that she's the one to pay for it. It would have been better if it happened to me.

Now I don't take anybody's word for anything. I've got a book on all the medicines and I check everything I'm prescribed. I question my doctor. Once you've been burned, you're not going to let somebody do that to you again.

Where are the lessons on DES at the conferences the doctors go to? DES definitely needs to be in the refresher courses, so that doctors will recognize people's symptoms when they see them. They need to see the human side to this—to see how not being sure of what they're prescribing can affect somebody's entire life.

—Claire Shaw

When Claire became pregnant with her first child, her husband was in medical school. His professor was an obstetrician who prescribed DES to Claire because she had previously miscarried. Fifteen years later Claire noticed Pennie's symptoms. She alerted her husband, who was by then an obstetrician himself. Pennie's father tested Pennie for gynecological problems. He diagnosed his own daughter with clear cell vaginal cancer and had to recommend her to a specialist for a complete hysterectomy at age 15. Pennie eventually married and adopted two children, now teenagers. Claire is a retired bank teller.

DES mother Claire Shaw, with daughter Pennie Judy

Exposed 1955

You just wanted to have me.
You didn't know what you were doing.

After my surgery I tried to protect my mother from how painful all of this felt. But at a certain point I stopped. I had faith that my mother would respect my tantrums.

Last year at Passover, I came in very depressed. It was a year and a month after my surgery. The family was coming over for a seder, and my best friend was pregnant and I had just found out. I walked in and I was angry, angry, angry. I was tired of always being happy for everybody's milestones.

I blew up and started crying, and I said, "I'm sick of it. I'm sick of other people having children. It's not fair. I want to be able to have a baby too. I'm sick of having to mourn for this. I'm just fed up and I'm angry." I kicked the bathroom door and I slammed doors in the house, and I marched up and down. My mother said, "Just cry, go ahead and have a good cry." I said, "I'm sorry I'm doing this in front of you." She said, "If you can't cry here, where are you going to cry?"

My mother has told me, "Don't you think that every time I see a pregnant woman, I get upset too? Don't you think I wake up every single day and think about your future and what I've done to you because of DES?" Then I'll say, "You didn't do anything to me. You just wanted to have me. You didn't know what you were doing."

—Judith Helfand

When Judith was 14 years old, she turned on the television to a talk show about DES. Horrified, she called her mother in to hear about this drug. That's when her mother told her that she, too, had taken DES.

Eleven years later, Judith met a woman working on a film about DES who encouraged Judith to have a medical exam. The doctor discovered that Judith had a rare cancer linked to DES exposure, clear cell cervical cancer. Judith underwent radical pelvic surgery. Her cervix, uterus, fallopian tubes and lymph nodes, as well as the top third of her vagina, were removed.

Judith, a filmmaker, is the producer of an award-winning film about DES called *A Healthy Baby Girl*.

DES daughter Judith Helfand, with mother, Florence Helfand

Exposed 1964

I thought I was strong because I didn't cry.

The scene at the hospital was horrible. The doctor called my parents in along with me. He didn't mince words at all. He said, "Laurie has cancer of the vagina from a pill that you took when you were carrying her." And my mother ran out of the room, screaming and crying, and I ran out following her, saying, "I'm here . . ."

I don't remember much after that. All I know is that I watched my parents age. Right there.

My parents moved into the hospital to be with me. I would wake up at 6:30 in the morning with someone taking blood and my father singing some ridiculous song to try to cheer me up.

When I went into the hospital, I thought I was strong because I didn't cry. But months passed, and my parents were concerned because I hadn't cried at all. One day my father walked into my room and closed the curtains and sat down.

He said that I was breaking his heart, because he wished it were him. And he said—he used to call me Skipper when I was little—he said, "I would do anything for you, Skipper, but what I can't heal here is a broken heart." And he said, "I think that's what's hurting you worst."

And when he said that, that was the first time I cried.

—Laurie Harrington

In her early twenties, Laurie Harrington discovered that she had clear cell cancer from her exposure to DES in utero. She received 25 radiation treatments, followed by a radiation implant inserted vaginally with five radium needles. Her treatments left Laurie with tissue burns, collapsed vaginal walls, and dysfunctional bowels. The lifelong complications remind Laurie of her DES exposure every day—a way, she says, of keeping things in perspective. She takes care of her chronic health problems with herbs and natural treatments.

Laurie works in the antiques business.

DES daughter Laurie Harrington

Exposed 1952

It seems a lot of questions about DES are taboo. Nobody wants to talk about it.

It seems a lot of questions about DES are taboo. Nobody wants to talk about it. As a DES son and cancer survivor, I want to know as much as I can, for my own peace of mind, because when I think about how much DES has affected my family, I feel profoundly sad.

For a lot of DES daughters, like my sister Kathleen, not being able to have children is so awful that it doesn't get talked about. I learned that guys can't talk about their testicles, period. Cancer or no cancer, you don't talk about it.

When I talk to my mom about DES, I am always so concerned that I not come across like I'm blaming her. She has such a hard time. If I start talking about DES in a way that shows my pain or anguish, she starts crying. She says, "I didn't know. I didn't mean to." And of course nobody's accusing her of anything. But her pain is huge.

If every woman who had taken this drug came forward and said, "Damn it, I want action," there would be action. But because there's so much shame and because nobody wants to blame their mother, it goes unspoken. Everyone just deals with their own health problems. We silently suffer through it. As long as that goes on, these drug companies will get away with murder.

—Bill Kenny

Bill happened to learn he had testicular cancer and was a DES son on the same day. He discovered a lump in his testicle in his early '30s. The few studies on DES sons have not shown a conclusive asssociation between DES and testicular cancer. At the advice of his sister Kathleen, a DES daughter who has lost three pregnancies because of DES injuries, Bill went to a urologist. Cancer was diagnosed. When Bill called to tell his parents he had cancer he learned that he was DES-exposed. Bill's testicle was surgically removed. He underwent chemotherapy and a testicular implant procedure. A year later Bill was diagnosed with a recurrence of the cancer. His remaining testicle was removed and he had extensive chemotherapy and surgical removal of his lymph nodes. After treatment, Bill returned to work as a freelance television writer.

DES son Bill Kenny, with mother, Mary Kenny, and sister Kathleen Sanderson

Exposed 1959

During the trial
I would wake up in the night screaming.

The lawsuit helped a lot. It allowed me to feel like I was doing something about DES. Unless people like me start talking, no one will know about DES and what it does to people's lives. I felt very strongly about being on the witness stand. I got up there thinking, "I can do this." But in many ways it was worse than having cancer.

My lawyer said, "Please tell us about when you first found out you had cancer." All the emotions that had been bottled up inside of me erupted. They just kept coming and coming. I wanted to tell my story but I couldn't stop crying. All the pain from over the years came up.

During the trial I would wake up in the night screaming. I absolutely hated the whole thing. At one point they brought in a doctor who testified that DES does not cause clear cell cancer. Later someone told me that the doctor had provided "expert testimony" for 30 other DES cases. I was told he earned about $8,000 every time he testified.

In the closing, in so many words, the defense lawyer called my mother a liar. "How could you remember the pills you took so many years ago?" he said.

One thing that really upset me was hearing some of the things my husband said on the witness stand. He warned me that he would be saying some things he had never told me. He told the jury that he can't look at my body the same way any more—that he looks at me and is reminded of the surgery.

—Margaret Perrotte

Margaret is the seventh of nine children. Her mother, Suzanne, was prescribed DES for all nine pregnancies. Two of Margaret's sisters are infertile. One of Margaret's brothers has a painful urogenital tract malformation that has required repeated medical intervention since he was a teenager.

Two years after she married, doctors discovered that Margaret had DES-related clear cell vaginal cancer. Surgeons performed a radical hysterectomy, lymphadenectomy, vaginectomy, and vaginal reconstruction.

Margaret filed a lawsuit against the company that manufactured and marketed the DES prescribed to her mother. Since then, she and her husband have adopted a baby boy from Romania.

Margaret works as a physical therapy assistant.

DES daughter Margaret Perrotte, with mother, Suzanne Munroe

Exposed 1962

I wish that I could go for one day and not think about what DES has meant in my life.

I knew what they were going to have to do—take out about 80 percent of the vagina, to the point where there was no sign of cancer. They used my stomach muscle to do a vaginal reconstruction. And they ended up taking out my uterus, a fallopian tube, part of my left ovary, and lymph nodes.

It was done pretty well. But they had to make a vertical incision rather than horizontal. It's about 10 inches long down the center of my abdomen and always a reminder. If I ever forget, for even a minute, that I had DES-related cancer, there is that horrifying scar.

Sometimes I wish for things that are really unrealistic. Like I wish that I could go for one day and not think about what DES has meant in my life. If I drew a circle, my identity as a DES cancer survivor would probably get 75 percent.

The people at the institutions that manufactured DES take no responsibility. And that just violates my whole experience. It takes it away at some level; it silences a part of my experience. And it's scary. Because it means we don't talk about DES very much. The lesson is not out there to be learned from.

I've had to ask myself deeper questions than I would have asked otherwise. I don't worry about the little things. I've come to see that you should not expect life on Earth to be perfect. I was given a different gift by having cancer so young: the gift of suffering and the gift of understanding people who are suffering—because I've been there, and I'm still there.

—Cynthia Wells

Cynthia learned she was DES-exposed when she was 16. The gynecologist was able to reassure Cynthia and her family that the risk for DES-related cancer was low. Research shows that only one out of every 1,000 DES daughters develops clear cell vaginal cancer. Over the following years Cynthia went regularly for checkups. She was treated for dysplasia, an abnormal change in the cervical cells, which is more common in DES daughters. Then, when Cynthia was in her mid-twenties, a biopsy of her vaginal tissue came back positive for clear cell cancer of the vagina. Surgeons immediately performed a radical hysterectomy, vaginectomy, and vaginal reconstruction to save her life.

Cynthia is an administrator at a private college.

DES daughter Cynthia Wells

Exposed 1966

To put it plainly, DES is a group I'd rather not belong to.

In pursuit of fertility, I had a shot in my tush with human conionic gonadatropin every three weeks for a year, to increase motility and count. I had two surgeries, called variococelectomies. They made an incision, cut the vein going into my testicle, and tied it off. It's been two surgeries, timed sex, lots of drugs, lots of money, lots of pain, and lots of time.

I don't know for sure if DES is the cause of my problems. There's not a lot of research on sons. What I do know is I'm DES-exposed.

We went to DES meetings but we couldn't handle them. We were in our twenties and early thirties, and people were dealing with malformed organs, cancer, hysterectomies, pregnancy losses. Brooke would come home and cry.

I tried to be that classically strong man who didn't talk about things. But I felt incredible guilt about being responsible for our infertility. I got distant and we almost lost our relationship. We both went into therapy because of DES. It feels like such loss of control. Loss of what it is to be a man, what it is to be a woman.

I've never met other DES-exposed men. It didn't matter to me about anyone else being DES-exposed. What mattered was my own situation and what might happen to Brooke. To put it plainly, DES is a group I'd rather not belong to. I was put in that position. I never think about DES except when I'm in the shower. Then I wonder, "Will I feel anything?"

In a positive way DES reconnected us and strengthened us. We overcame something dealt to us and we've been able to survive and continue life. We've been through so much we feel we can handle anything. Our luck is we arrived at our daughter, Arley. She is healthy and smart and life came about, but in a different way. We think of her like a flower blooming in the garden, and we don't know what flower she is.

—Richie Hare

Richie and Brooke are both DES-exposed. They joke that they ran a personal ad, "DES son looking for DES daughter." When they didn't conceive by their late '20s, Richie and Brooke had a fertility exam and Richie was diagnosed as infertile. Most research, however, does not show infertility in DES sons.

Richie had an obstruction causing pooling of blood in his testicles. His sperm was slow and malformed; his count was low. For eight years he underwent treatment, including fertility drugs and surgery.

Brooke's doctors told her she had a "classic DES" uterus and an incompetent cervix, and that if she did get pregnant the baby would not reach full term. For 15 years Brooke has had an annual DES exam; her most recent colposcopy showed some cell changes.

Richie is a school psychologist and Brooke a school social worker. They adopted their daughter, Arley, as an infant. Arley is in 7th grade and loves swimming and pets.

DES son Richie Hare, with wife, DES daughter Brooke Gordon-Hare, and daughter, Arley

Exposed 1951

I discovered a tornado at the base of my cervix.

At one point I said to the universe, "What else can you do to mutilate me, to hurt me?" I was angry at the men I'd broken up with, wondering if I would ever have children.

Having only part of a cervix is painful sexually, and makes me afraid of the pain. It makes me feel like I'm not what I could be.

Eventually I got into psychoanalysis and energy work. During one session, I did craniosacral work, a kind of healing massage. I discovered a tornado at the base of my cervix. It extended upwards toward my head, and every coil of the tornado had anger.

I was angry at the researchers who made the drug and the reps who sold the drug. I was angry at the doctors for giving DES to my mom. I was angry at my mother for taking it. I felt anger for everything that had been done to me. And for everything that had been done there was another circle of the tornado.

I had to do a lot of forgiving. I had always wanted kids so badly.

I'm a strong believer in body-mind unity, and one time I was able to get in touch with the emotional memory of my body. The idea is to access a memory and release its painful emotion. I traveled back to when I was an embryo, through my conception and gestation and birth. I could feel my mother's fear. She had lost a baby before me. I understood why she took the DES. I saw my uterus and ovaries and fallopian tubes being formed. They were new and crystalline and pure and they were the most beautiful things.

Now, my path is to help people keep control of their bodies and listen to what their bodies are telling them. I talk to my ovaries and they talk to me. They say, "I want kale." So I feed them kale.

Everything we do affects the world around us. We have to take responsibility for what we do to our bodies and what we do to the Earth. That's the big lesson of DES.

—Diane Vermillion

Diane's mother accompanied her to her first gynecology exam at age 15. "You have erosion of the cervix because of the DES your mother took," the doctor said. He was the same doctor who had prescribed the DES.

In college, Diane was diagnosed with cervical dysplasia. She has undergone repeated laser surgery and cryosurgery to remove the abnormal cells.

When the treatments did not eradicate the dysplasia, Diane was advised to have cervical conization. Under general anesthesia, a conical wedge was cut out of the center of her cervix. This caused a severe narrowing of her cervix, and debilitating menstrual cycles.

Unfortunately, Diane's dysplasia returned. Her doctors recommended removing the entire cervix, but Diane wanted children so badly she pleaded to keep her cervix.

Diane is a professor of anatomy and physiology at a university, with a private practice in healing therapies. She has no children.

DES daughter Diane Vermillion

Exposed 1952

I have a deeper understanding of the meaning of sex.

When John and I were dating, I was always sick. I had severe bladder infections from the radiation and problems with the estrogen replacement dose. On one hand, I didn't want to tell him about DES. On the other hand, I wanted to tell him, "This is a part of who I am, and I think you need to know."

John was shocked. He said, "Boy, this is like that thalidomide stuff over in West Germany." I said, "Yeah, this is the American thalidomide."

It was years before I could even say where the cancer was. I was horrified to not only have cancer and lose my fertility, but—because of where it was—have the impact on my sexual functioning.

Your picture of yourself as a sexual being is formed throughout your life. Getting vaginal cancer in your twenties is like dropping a bomb in the middle of the whole process. It's not just the physical pain. Suddenly a whole lot of people were part of a conversation about my sexuality. I was having conversations I never imagined in my lifetime, let alone with the people I was talking to.

No experience in life can prepare you for this. So many doctors and interns were examining my vagina, I had to desensitize myself to get through it. You go into shock.

A year after the radiation, I began to feel worse effects. Chemo kills the cells all at once, but radiation kills cells over time. My vagina started to hurt more and more. Intercourse was very painful and I'd bleed a lot. It would freak me out, and I'd think, "Oh my God. I'll never be able to have sex again." It was hugely important for me to get back to normal sexual functioning.

I was 29 when I got DES cancer. I was raised to believe sex was healthy and okay, and I was old enough to have enjoyed my sexuality for a few years. But for girls who had this cancer as teenagers—I can't imagine how awful. You'd be just feeling out your sexual self and it blows up in your face.

The feeling of being able to trust my body to express closeness and joy and love was changed by DES and cancer. I had to monitor my body, rather than let it go. I was always thinking, "I hope it's not going to hurt too much." My doctor was great. He said, "Listen, honey, I wish I could write you a prescription for a lover. You need to keep it working."

—story continued on page 42

In her early twenties, LuEllen was told she had a malformed cervix and might have a difficult time carrying a baby to term; her doctor wrote "probable DES exposure" on her chart. At 29, LuEllen was diagnosed with clear cell vaginal cancer. She received five weeks of radiation treatment, then 30 hours of cesium implant, in which a radioactive substance is inserted in the vagina and sewn in place. LuEllen lost her ability to have children and the functioning of her ovaries, and she had to start taking estrogen replacement medication while still in her twenties. LuEllen suffers complications from radiation, including vaginal and bladder shrinkage and intestinal problems. A few months after the diagnosis, LuEllen's mother located the medical records documenting that she was prescribed DES, starting in her ninth week of pregnancy.

LuEllen is a realtor and a private pilot. Her husband, John, is a flight instructor. Together they practice and compete in aerobatic flying maneuvers.

DES daughter LuEllen Blum, with husband, John Blum

Exposed 1954

DES daughter LuEllen Blum (continued)

I found a partner in John, who accepts and enjoys all of me. He asks questions and we work through things together. There are times when it's frustrating. Radiation causes shrinkage and scarring. Lots of little nerve endings aren't active anymore. But we make it satisfying on every level.

John and I have had to talk about sex a lot. If you want to pick up the pieces of your life and go on, you have to talk. You have to let go of shyness and discuss what you need and want.

I know many DES daughters. The ones who've decided to take it and keep going and growing are exceptional people. I like to think this trickles down to the sexual level too. We are exceptional people sexually. Yes, I lost some spontaneity and carefree attitude about my body, compared to somebody who's never had any DES exposure. But maybe I gained something. Maybe my sexuality is better than it would have been. Out of something so negative, something positive can come. For one thing, I'm more open about sex. My identity as a sexual being has a special place in my life. I don't take it for granted. I have a deeper understanding of the meaning of sex. I realize how important sexuality is for people. And I'm more appreciative of the subtle nuances of sex. It's the little things that are the nicest.

I tend to use my experience with DES to build me into a better, stronger person. I use it to choose people who are worthy of me and my time—and worthy of my affection. Now, I'm finding my '40s more enjoyable in every sense, including my sexuality. It comes from physically accepting where I am, and making the most of it.

After cancer I had to figure out how to live again and be happy. I had to rely on myself to accept the whole DES thing. I thought, "Why am I looking to everybody else for happiness? Nobody can do it for me." At a certain point I just decided to be happy.

I like to think I would have been comfortable sexually, anyway. But I have to admit, I'm probably more so because of what happened to me. You get thrown into the fire of DES exposure, and what doesn't break you makes you stronger.

—LuEllen Blum

*T*hose considering the wisdom of precautionary action today would do well to consider the history of DES. This drug was a known animal carcinogen, a suspect human carcinogen, and a drug that had been shown to produce observable changes in the offspring of women exposed in pregnancy. . . . Had DES been withdrawn for use . . . the unnecessary and tragic exposure of millions of mothers, sons, and daughters could have been avoided.

—Dolores Ibarreta, Ph.D., and
Shanna H. Swan, Ph.D.

It doesn't look like there's much to worry about being that you're a boy.

I was in summer camp and got a letter from my mother with a clipping of a newspaper article. She wrote, "You should be aware of this. I think I took this drug when I was pregnant with you. But it doesn't look like there's much to worry about being that you're a boy." I was about 13. I probably read it, laughed, scratched my head, and ran off to play softball.

A few years later, when I was a junior in high school, I found myself with a mysterious inability to urinate. I was in tremendous pain and woke my parents up at three in the morning. They took me to the emergency ward. I was catheterized and had to stay in the hospital for a week.

Every day since then I've had some difficulty urinating. Since the age of 16, I've felt a little bit like a guy in his sixties with prostate problems. I've told doctors, "I'm exposed to DES, and I had this problem when I was a kid, and I wonder what it has to do with what's going on now." And they go, "Uh-huh, uh-huh." And shake their heads and feel my pulse.

I never connected it to DES, but for a time, around puberty, I remember wishing I was a girl. I had a secret doll collection along with my puppet collection, and I didn't relate to other guys. I just thought I would fit in better as a girl. I grew out of it, but I can't help but wonder. How much did DES have to do with it? If you're a little male fetus and you're getting shot up with all this estrogen for three months, it could have an effect on your hormonal system. Who knows? Maybe it has nothing to do with DES. Maybe it does.

—Warren Lehrer

Warren, a writer, learned about DES at the age of 13, when his mother told him she had taken DES every day for three months during her pregnancy with him. Warren has a history of spinal, urinary tract, and autoimmune problems that have been seen in other DES-exposed people. At the age of 16, he was hospitalized with an inability to urinate and has had difficulty ever since.

Warren, who is married, has concerns about his ability to father a child, and has tried to find out if his medical problems are related to his DES exposure.

DES son Warren Lehrer

Exposed 1949

What DES exposure has done for me is change my view of the world.

I talk about DES to other people. A lot of them think it's all in the past. Why bring it up now? It's all over with. I don't think it's all over with. First of all, each of us will have to live with the effects forever. And I'm not so sure that all the effects are known.

Since we had the effects 20 and 30 years after exposure, why not 50 years later? I don't go around worrying, but it's a possibility.

I have worked in medicine and seen it in action. I know for sure that doctors and other health professionals aren't always people you should put on a pedestal. What DES exposure has done for me is change my view of the world. I'm very wary anytime I hear, "Oh, we know all about that. It can't hurt you."

I talk to people who say, "Oh yeah, my mother thinks she took that." But they're not having any problems, so that's as far as it goes. I think to myself, "You should consider yourself lucky that you don't have to know about this."

If I had died, people would have been sad. But I wouldn't have to be fighting this any more—all these things that have happened to my body. I wasn't angry having to come back. I was disappointed. Now I'm not afraid of dying; I'm only afraid of what might happen before I get to that point.

—Marilyn Ehler

Marilyn was a medical dosimetrist for nine years, planning radiation therapy for cancer patients. She was inspired to pursue this career because of her own radiation treatment for DES-related cancer in her twenties, which included seven surgeries and radiation implants. During one surgery Marilyn went into cardiac failure and almost died. Eventually she had to stop work because of her combined medical problems from DES exposure and diabetes.

Marilyn continued with her love of singing in a community chorus. At age 45, she died from cardiac arrest related to complications from diabetes.

DES daughter Marilyn Ehler, with mother, Helen Ferguson

Exposed 1954

I wish someone would come to my door and say, "Hello, I am responsible."

About eight years after my surgery and radiation treatments, my legs started to hurt. They were swelling and it got to the point where they were too large for pants. It was never explained to me that this might occur as a result of having my lymph glands removed. Now I have a constant daily reminder of my DES exposure. I have to wrap my left leg in tight elastic stockings, think about whether I have the best compression, elevate my leg all night, and use a pump twice a day to remove the fluid. I can't sit for long periods, I can't stand for long periods, and I can't move around as freely as I want. My leg is tender and sore. I can't get it sunburned, and I can't risk infection.

You just have to deal with it daily. It's never, "OK, when I reach September 12 it will all be over, and I've lived through it." There's no "OK, because you're DES-exposed, we want you to have this wonderful vacation." There's no reward there.

I do wish someone would apologize. I wish someone would come to my door and say, "Hello, I am responsible, and I am so sorry this happened to you." It is a he. He would knock on my door and say, "Jeannette Travis? My name is David Edison Smith—hi, I'm DES—and I did this to you, and I'm so sorry."

Lately I've been focusing more on what we can expect. I've been through the surgery; I've had radiation treatments. I've lived that, so now what? Answers, that's what I need. I don't want another surprise. Just plain old facts would be good. And then I'll deal with them as best I can.

—Jeannette Travis

Jeannette's doctors were slow to diagnose her DES-related clear cell vaginal cancer, in the 1970s, due to its rarity. In her early twenties she underwent a radical hysterectomy, vaginectomy, and lymphadenectomy. After the surgery, Jeannette was treated with radiation implants. Some years later, she developed lymphedema, a painful swelling in her legs brought about by the removal of her lymph nodes.

Jeannette, an elementary school teacher, is married; she and her husband have not adopted any children. She says her happiness never hinged on having children, but she would have liked to have had the choice.

DES daughter Jeannette Travis

Exposed 1950

Hindsight is better than foresight by a damn sight.

I'm the father. Not the one who had to take the medication. But I know how much Jane wanted that baby. And so did I. Without DES I might not have a daughter. All I can tell you is my experience. And my experience is I'd do it again because I have Lisa.

I've heard the studies saying DES didn't work and I don't know whether to believe it. Statistics don't mean anything in an individual case. Who the hell knows who's right? It's a matter of opinion. It looked like DES saved the pregnancy.

Hindsight is better than foresight by a damn sight. I was a pediatrician. I loved babies. But you make these choices and you either make yourself miserable or you make peace with it. At my age you make peace with it.

Sure, Lisa had no choice. Her mother took the DES. She didn't ask Lisa.

Lisa has had some hard times. Over the years she has come up tails several times more than the average. It's not been easy. She's been on bed rest for months at a time.

I'd sweat out her miscarriages—when she'd call from the hospital—and there were several of them.

I hope people who read these stories don't think they did the wrong thing. Especially the women who took the pill. Why throw gasoline on a fire now? A mother might think, "What have I done? Where's the cyanide?" Or some kid could read it and think, "God damn my mother. Why did she do it?"

Life is a feeling thing. It's 90% emotional. What's important is to avoid "Poor me. Why me?" Well, why not me? It happens.

I hope my story can help someone feel better about the whole deal. People can be helped to see that DES happens to millions of people, people who took it in good faith. I have no ax to grind. I'm telling my story to help people make peace for themselves, not to throw stones.

—Jud Speer

Jud was in medical school in 1955. His wife, Jane, was pregnant for the first time. She began to have some bleeding, so her doctor put her on bed rest, and prescribed DES. Lisa was born later that year.

It was Jud who told Lisa, when she was a teenager, about her DES exposure, and made sure she saw a gynecologist. At first it was scary for Lisa to think she could get cancer from DES, but over time she felt lucky to know about her exposure so she could get appropriate medical care.

Lisa has been pregnant seven times. She has had three early miscarriages and one miscarriage at five months. She was diagnosed with a typical DES-incompetent cervix, which caused premature effacement and dilation during her successful pregnancies. She was sewn up with a cerclage, monitored for shortening and opening of the cervix, and put on bed rest.

Jud's grandchildren are nine, five, and two years old. He is a retired pediatrician.

DES father Judson Speer, M.D.

Daughter exposed 1955

It was easier talking about DES than telling him where babies come from.

I took DES during the whole pregnancy with my oldest son, Joseph. I was spotting and that was the way they treated you. DES was the drug of choice. They thought it would keep you from losing your baby. Now they know it didn't work at all.

When I got pregnant in 1971, I started on DES again. A month later my doctor took me off it when he heard the news about DES and cancer. As information started coming out I was very worried that Joseph would be infertile or have malformations. If anything went wrong I felt it would be my fault.

I broached the subject with the pediatrician. He said, "He's only six. We'll keep an eye on him."

When Joseph was around 15 I told him about DES. It was easier talking about DES than telling him where babies came from, I'll tell you that. His reaction was, "Oh Ma, don't be ridiculous. I'm perfectly fine. I'm healthy."

It was difficult to tell my sons. But I'd rather they were aware than hiding their heads in the sand. If someone needs to know something, we're going to talk about it. Even if it's difficult.

I used to tell the boys when they had to get an injection, "You're going to have a shot. It's going to hurt, but it's important for your health." That's how I feel about DES. It may hurt to learn about DES; it may be scary. But at least you'll know enough to follow up and get the right care.

When Joseph got engaged we discussed it again. I felt he should tell his fiancée. That's when I knew she was the right person. She said, "I love him. It doesn't matter whether we can have children or not." They are very fortunate because they have two beautiful children. And my younger son, Jonathan, who was exposed for one month? He's fine, too.

—Kathryn Zenevitch

Kathryn was pregnant for the first time in 1965, with her son Joseph. Her doctor prescribed DES every day for eight months. The pills were bright red. "Some days I don't remember my name," said Kathryn, "but I'll never forget those little red pills."

When Kathryn became pregnant with her son Jonathan, her doctor again prescribed DES. But he took her off the pills soon after reading a study showing DES linked to cancer in daughters exposed in utero.

Neither of Kathryn's sons have experienced health problems related to their DES exposure, though Kathryn was diagnosed with breast cancer in her mid '50s. She was treated with a lumpectomy, followed by chemotherapy, six weeks of radiation, and tamoxifen. She has been cancer-free for two years.

At the time of her interview, neither Kathryn nor her physician were aware that studies show DES mothers to have an increased risk of breast cancer.

Kathryn is an administrative assistant in a community hospital.

DES mother Kathryn Zenevitch, with son Jonathan Zenevitch

Exposed 1971

I take it hard
that my doctor doesn't believe I was exposed.

I go to a family doctor and I've mentioned the DES a couple of times, wondering if she should do something special. But she says it's impossible—they didn't give DES past 1969. I take it hard that my doctor doesn't believe I was exposed. I think it's a big deal that all the women and children were exposed. I think it's terrible.

The Planned Parenthood doctor I first went to in high school said I'm definitely exposed because of the shape of my cervix. And I have vaginal cells on the cervix and cervical cells on my vagina.

I've never met another DES daughter. Actually, I probably have, but I wouldn't know it because no one ever talks about it. I even wrote a term paper on it because I wanted more information. You never hear the same thing from people about DES.

When I got pregnant I reminded the ob-gyn that I had been exposed. He blew me off, saying the same thing about the date. But one day he was out of town and another doctor did the internal exam.

Thank God he did. I was 28 weeks pregnant and totally effaced, turned out, and 1.5 cm dilated. He said, "You're on complete bed rest until the end of the pregnancy."

I lay on my back for three months. I hurt so bad. I called the doctor and begged him to let me off. My muscles were atrophying. I could only sit up for 15 minutes every two hours. I couldn't do stairs, laundry, dishes. You take a healthy 22-year-old and make her lie down for three months. It hurts. But I wanted this baby so bad after thinking I might never have one that I wouldn't jeopardize her.

When I heard about the study in mice suggesting DES granddaughter mice have more tumors, I got scared again. What will it mean for Brianna? I guess no one knows. But now I feel a little bit of what my own mother must feel. And I've got to tell my daughter about DES so she will know and be aware.

—Kelly Platt

In 1970, Kelly's mother, Donna, was pregnant for the third time. Her doctor prescribed what he called "a small wonder drug."

Sixteen years later, Kelly went for her first gynecologic exam. "Your insides don't look normal," the doctor said. "Did your mother take DES when she was pregnant?"

Kelly had never heard of DES. But her mother remembered taking little white pills and felt "scared to death."

Kelly and Donna talk a lot about DES. What upsets Donna the most is knowing that the popularity of DES was waning by the time she was prescribed it in 1970.

Coincidentally, Kelly married a man who is also DES-exposed. His mother told him about his exposure the day she learned that Kelly was expecting.

As Kelly learns more about DES, she is seeking a physician who is knowledgeable about DES and can provide good follow-up care for DES daughters.

Kelly is a manicurist. Her daughter, Brianna, is six years old.

DES daughter Kelly Platt, with daughter, Brianna

Exposed 1970

This was an injustice.
There's nothing you are at fault for.

After losing the fetus, people didn't want me to talk about it. I thought, why shouldn't I be talking about it? This was a loss for me. It was taken from me, not because of something I'd done, but because of DES.

We're made to feel our sexuality and reproduction are not meant to be talked about. As girls, when we first get our periods, we are told to keep it quiet. Then we're made to feel embarrassed to talk if we have a miscarriage or reproductive calamity. Voices should never be silent. Telling the stories of DES is a way of educating people. We can learn from DES because someday there will be something else like DES again.

Many people are embarrassed to talk about DES. I know a DES daughter who is a clergy and is unwilling to talk about it, even though she's had children. She doesn't want DES as part of her public identity. She thinks it's exposing her reproductive life and sexuality in ways she doesn't want. I say it's crazy. It would give comfort to people to know they are not alone in this. It's nothing to feel embarrassed about. Let's not confuse it. This was an injustice that was done to you. There's nothing you are at fault for.

DES has had a tremendous impact on how I look at the world. I won't take estrogen during menopause because I think women are led down the garden path of overmedication. And I'm more of an advocate in general. I don't assume that decisions are made in the best interests of the individual.

Companies make mistakes. We all make mistakes. But if you walk away from your mistakes and don't take responsibility, that is a problem. Think what a difference it would be, in terms of people's suffering, if drug companies took some responsibility for DES. They could have funded a program to notify people. As it is, many people don't know they are exposed. If people knew they were exposed, their cancer might have been diagnosed earlier and they might not have died.

—Marcy Gilbert

Marcy was born in Montreal. Her mother, who had had a miscarriage, was given DES by injection and tablets throughout her pregnancy with Marcy.

Marcy's mother started taking her to the gynecologist in third grade. It was hard for her to talk about DES. She would say, "Don't blame me. I didn't mean to. I just wanted you so much."

Marcy lost one pregnancy because of her DES-weakened cervix, then gave birth to her first son after a stressful, closely monitored pregnancy. She declined intervention the next time, and sailed through what she calls "a lovely pregnancy." Marcy's sons are now teenagers.

Marcy credits DES Action Canada for bringing DES to public attention in that country, where an estimated 200,000–400,000 women were prescribed DES.

Marcy works as a consultant to the not-for-profit sector.

DES daughter Marcy Gilbert

Exposed 1956

I ask for a recognition of Betsy's life and death.

During the deposition I just wanted to hear the drug company lawyers say they understood us. I didn't ask them to say the companies did anything wrong.

I asked them to go the drugstore and get a card. I asked them to write, "We here, at such and such a company, express our condolences at the loss of your sister, Betsy Wood."

But they wouldn't do it. They were afraid I would turn their condolences into a media event.

It felt in a small way what a rape victim must go through. They bring up ugly and embarrassing things and mistakes you've made in your life and rake you over the coals. It made my dad cry. It made me furious and upset.

Betsy and I were little brother and big sister arguers. We hiked the Appalachian Trail together when I was 18. Just me and Betsy. We had great discussions and arguments about everything. She'd get on me about smoking and say, "The clean air was here first." She was big into clean water and skinny dipping in the woods. She loved the sound of a brook. She always said, "What was here first, goes first." Her idea was that somebody's got to watch out for it.

Betsy found out she had cancer from DES when she was 18. They gave her a partial vaginectomy. I can't even fathom it. I mean how would you feel? She got really healthy through a macrobiotic diet and fresh juices and tons of garlic. But then she went back to school to do her M.A., and got back into junk food. It's harder than you think to eat right and treat yourself right in today's fast-paced world.

When the cancer came back Betsy was angry at herself. She thought she'd misrepresented how eating right could keep you healthy. She never acknowledged she was dying. She'd act like things were going to be okay. But you'd hear her in the shower yelling at herself to fight the cancer. In the end she wouldn't take morphine. She wanted to be mentally alert.

—Jonathan Wood

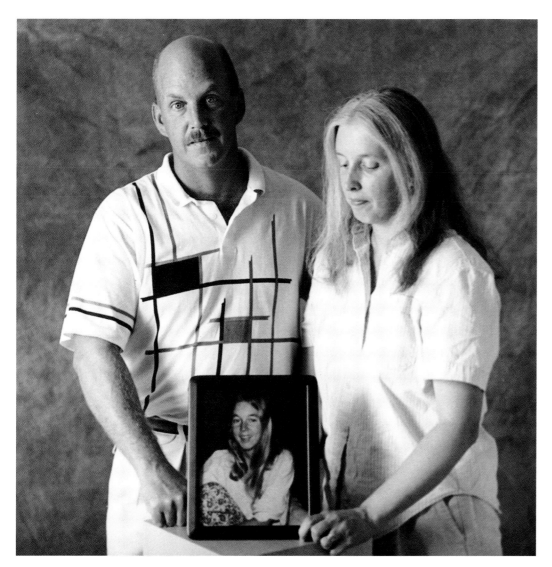

Susan was the first in the family to find out she was DES-exposed. Her mother remembered taking DES with her, and they found her medical records. Then her mother remembered taking DES with Betsy and Jonathan.

Jonathan, the youngest, was 13 when he was told that he and his sisters were DES-exposed. From infancy until age six, one of his testicles was undescended. At 23 he was diagnosed with embryonial cell testicular cancer in the same testicle. After surgery to remove the testicle, Jonathan had eight weeks of intensive chemotherapy. He is now cancer-free and the father of a 3-year-old daughter.

Betsy, the oldest of the three, was 22 and in college when she was diagnosed with vaginal clear cell adenocarcinoma. Her tumor was cut out locally and surgeons performed a partial vaginectomy.

—bio continued on page 61

DES son Jonathan Wood, with sister, DES daughter Susan Wood, holding a photograph of their deceased sister, DES daughter Betsy Wood

Exposed 1962, 1958, and 1956

Betsy taught me that everything is interwoven.

Betsy didn't want anything to do with being a cancer patient. She was an environmentalist and her passion was the natural world. She worked to save the wilderness from overdevelopment.

My personal reason for telling our story is to memorialize Betsy and the lives of all people who have suffered from DES. My public motivation is I want to get information out and put a face on DES; to warn other women and men to get proper care and arm themselves with knowledge. I also want to alert people to chemical exposure, be it DES or other chemicals in our environment.

What I feel about DES is a combination of outrage and regret. I feel individual sorrow for each member of my family. Hundreds of thousands of us shouldn't have been exposed in the first place. DES should have been pulled off the market in 1953—after the Dieckmann study at the University of Chicago showed DES to be ineffective in the prevention of miscarriage.

One thing Betsy taught me is that the environment is a complex web of life; everything is interwoven. DES is not an isolated incident.

Hormone exposure is a big question mark—whether you get it through DES, estrogen replacement therapy, spilling in the wetlands, or endocrine-disrupting chemicals in industrial products. On a larger scale, DES is what's happening in our environment. Exposures to chemicals that mimic estrogens are causing sickness and dysfunction in wildlife and humans, just like DES harmed us. Environmental exposures are small in comparison to DES, but multiple exposures may add up and have a stronger effect. We can't oversimplify and say it's no problem. Our models aren't sophisticated enough to predict the outcomes of chemical pollution. I think we need to use our best science with our best intuition to remember that everything is interwoven. If you make a disturbance in one area, it can have consequences far beyond.

—Susan Wood

DES daughter Susan Wood

bio contined from page 59

Betsy worked as an environmentalist. She was dedicated to wildlife habitat preservation and led a successful campaign to protect the Durbin Swamp wetlands, in northeast Florida, from being turned into landfill. She died from DES-related cancer at age 34.

Susan was diagnosed with adenosis as a teenager and later learned she has a T-shaped uterus. At 28 she experienced a near fatal ectopic pregnancy. Her abdomen was opened under general anesthesia and the embryo and fallopian tube were removed. With only one fallopian tube, conceiving takes about twice as long for Susan. After many years, she gave birth to a daughter, Betty, who is named after her Aunt Betsy.

Jonathan owns a property management company. Susan is the director of the Office of Women's Health for the FDA.

Is it the DES I was exposed to? Is it the water I'm drinking?

I try not to focus on it. But if you sit still it upsets you. What on earth is happening that I would have breast cancer so young, and so seriously? Is it the DES I was exposed to? Is it the water I'm drinking?

There's no history of breast cancer in my family. I had my children in my '20s, and you're at higher risk if you have children late in life.

I've been on a mission to erase any chance of the cancer coming back. The worst part was the pain from the chemotherapy. My whole body would hurt from head to toe. I'd just lie on the couch and cry.

Every time I read that DES is linked to increased breast cancer in DES mothers, I wonder if it's linked to breast cancer in DES daughters.

I'd like to see scientists continue to research breast cancer in daughters. We daughters are still young. Maybe the research hasn't caught up with us yet. After all, it took a while to compile our reproductive problems and say, "DES daughters are having pregnancy problems."

I'd like to see researchers go to breast cancer patients and families of the deceased, and ask about a history of DES exposure. I also want DES daughters to check themselves. The last thing on my mind was checking my breasts.

What's really hard is I can't have any more kids. But I see so many DES daughters having fertility problems. It's got to be terrible to not ever experience being pregnant.

Right now I'm regaining my strength. It's taking a long time. I guess you could say my youth was stolen from me. I'm in my mid '30s on the outside, but I feel about 57 inside. On the positive side, I've pushed myself quite a bit and made it through this ordeal. I know I'm strong, and I've made many good friends.

—Colleen Bracci

Colleen learned she was exposed to DES when she was diagnosed with an incompetent cervix and a uterus that was split down the middle.

Due to these structural problems, Colleen miscarried her first two pregnancies. Subsequently, she was able to carry two pregnancies to term; her children are seven and 11.

In her early '30s, Colleen was diagnosed with Stage 3 breast cancer. Her right breast was removed, followed by months of chemotherapy and radiation treatment.

About the same time, her Pap smears began to come back positive. Doctors recommended a hysterectomy and Colleen had her uterus and ovaries removed. Eleven months later, as a preventive measure, Colleen underwent surgery to remove her remaining breast. That breast turned out to have cancerous cells as well.

During her medical treatment, Colleen took a leave of absence from her real estate work. She is feeling healthier every day.

DES daughter Colleen Bracci

Exposed 1966

It's not something I can wrap up in a tiny package and put in the past.

I feel like a walking time bomb. I have a gynecologist who's been saying for three years, "We'll have to keep an eye on you." I say, "What does that mean? One of these days we'll ring the fire alarm and do something? Should I voluntarily have a hysterectomy? Or do I wait until it hits the red zone?" When I go to the doctor I feel like a kid again, exactly like I did when I had DES cancer. In a sense, I feel like my mom, because I think, "I need to trust you. Tell me what to do, and I'll do it."

The effects of my exposure are not something that I can spend years in therapy on and get over. It's not something that I can wrap up in a tiny package and put in the past. The worst part of the whole experience is the shame. Even now, 20-plus years later, I keep it in a shameful place. Maybe five other people in my world know. And it is me forcing it back; me not sharing, keeping it in my hiding place.

I would love to rant and rave to the world, to talk about it in a detached manner so that people know how rotten and terrible DES is. But to talk about what happened to my body? That's hard for me.

Without a husband or children, I've had to forgive myself for not living up to other people's opinions. I'm finally past the no-kids thing. I'm coming to a place where I recognize my strengths and like myself. DES is not the only battle you have to fight. I've fought so many battles and I've won every one. No matter what—I'll always have my spirit, and my laughter.

—Georgiann Kensinger

Georgiann was the only child, out of eight in her family, to be exposed in utero to DES. At the age of 15 Georgiann was diagnosed with DES-related clear cell cervical cancer. The cancer was treated with surgery, radiation, and radium implants. Recent medical exams show recurrence of abnormal cervical cell growth; Georgiann is deciding whether to have more medical treatment or to wait and watch.

Georgiann is a contract negotiator in the health care industry.

DES daughter Georgiann Kensinger

Exposed 1959

I've come a long way.

When I think about having another child, my biggest fear is putting the baby through pain.

Everett had so many IVs in him they ran out of arteries and had to use his head. It got to the point where he didn't cry anymore when they put another needle in.

He wants a brother or sister desperately and I never intended to have an only child. But when I think about another child, I can feel so vulnerable and defective. People tell me, "You deserve the chance to have a normal pregnancy." Well, maybe I deserve it, but can I do it? I don't know.

I'd like to see statistics on how many DES daughters have children with birth-related defects. More reproductive problems than we realize may be linked to chemical exposures.

Everett is nine now. He's bright and articulate. He was developmentally delayed but he's caught up. He's at zero percentile for height and weight and at 48 pounds he can wear the same clothes he wore four years ago. But I have a beautiful son and I know God has a plan for him. He went through so much to be here.

The repercussions of my exposure are with me daily. I have felt defective from DES. If you're feeling defective about yourself you're going to act it out. With help, I am learning to love myself and trust others and live one day at a time.

I want to feel like DES is not a secret. I want to get it out in the open, as opposed to letting it sit there, festering. It terrifies me that DES is so secret and never gets talked about. We don't have to be silent about it.

I've come a long way by getting DES out in the open so I can process it and move on. The only way to get through DES is to go through it.

—Sue Froh

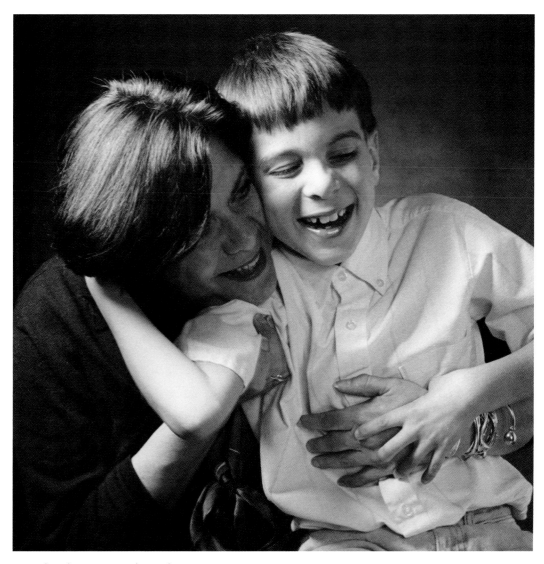

Sue's mom was 23, and had no history of pregnancy problems when she was prescribed DES.

Sue and her mom rarely talked about DES before her mother died. Sue felt it was an unspoken agreement that she protect her mother by not bringing it up.

Sue's cervix has the typical DES structural and cellular changes of ridges and adenosis. Her first pregnancy miscarried because of what doctors called a "DES uterus." When she became pregnant again, she was confined to bed rest for six months, and outfitted with an electronic device to alert nearby medical staff to uterine contractions.

Despite precautions, Sue's malformed uterus could not hold her pregnancy to term. Everett was born six weeks early, at four pounds. He underwent three surgeries before he was six months old.

Stress contributed to an amicable divorce between Sue and her husband when Everett was two.

Sue is an administrator at a large university.

DES daughter Sue Froh, with son, Everett

Exposed 1962

I wanted to spend the rest of my life with her.

I would probably have gone through my life never knowing about DES, except that I fell in in love with a DES daughter.

We were dating seriously, and one day, out of the blue, Roz called and said, "I have to see you." We met outside the bank where she works, and she handed me a big manila folder. I thought, "Why are you giving me your medical history?"

Roz told me about DES this way: "There will be an ongoing risk of cancer and potential to never have a natural child." Because of this, she would want to pursue adoption.

She was almost contrite, and sad, in revealing this part of her. Almost like I'd reject her. But this is a woman I am very attracted to; a special, unique person. I wanted to spend the rest of my life with her. Because of who she is. Not because of her plumbing. If my wife told me she had a disability, or was on medication, why would it be an issue?

I've learned there's a tremendous amount of sadness around being DES-exposed—a lot of self-criticism. Roz's mother feels responsible for Roz's medical condition and Katie's future. The fear and uncertainty is an added dimension. You're never quite sure which health problems are related.

We both wanted to have a child together. We tried for 18 months to get pregnant, but it wan't working. The doctors all said they could see no medical reason, but of course there was always the nagging doubt that there was something wrong with Roz.

Then, the month we gave up taking Clomid and decided to focus on adoption Roz became pregnant. I was filled with joy and so astounded.

But God, it was not a relaxed pregnancy. Roz had two serious hemorrhages, in which she lost so much blood the doctors didn't know if the baby would survive. I'll never forget seeing Katie's tiny arm waving across the ultrasound screen after we thought we'd lost her.

—story continued on page 70

When Roz was 11, Roz's mother told her she was a DES daughter. In her twenties, Roz was diagnosed with pre-cancerous, cervical dysplasia, which was treated extensively with laser surgery. She also learned she had a T-shaped uterus.

Roz's first marriage ended in divorce, partly due to the stress of infertility. Happily remarried, and determined to have children, Roz began, with Andy, to start on the difficult journey of coming to terms with her potential infertility. They tried artificial insemination and several rounds of Clomid. Just as they were giving up hope of conceiving, Roz became pregnant. After two hemorrhages, she was put on bed rest, then hospitalized. Daughter Katie was born premature at 35 weeks.

Roz is a vice president of a community bank. Andy is a management consultant for a Fortune 500 company.

Andy Zatyko with wife, DES daughter Roz Zatyko, and daughter, Katie

Wife exposed 1962

DES husband Andy Zatyko (continued)

When the doctor put Roz on bed rest I set up mission control. I put a mini refrigerator next to the bed and the computer on a cocktail table. Every morning I made her breakfast, lunch, and dinner, and put a movie in the VCR. Her assistant came over first thing and prepped her on the day. Her work kept her from going nuts.

DES becomes a man's issue when he's sharing his life with a woman who is DES-exposed. I find myself incredibly sensitive to how Roz is feeling. I'm the one who says, "Come on. Go to the doctor," when she puts off going.

I feel profound admiration for my wife for getting through this and bringing our daughter into the world in spite of it all. The shame and lingering guilt doesn't have to be there. Everyone is a tapestry made up of different pieces. That's what makes you interesting. DES is part of Roz's tapestry. If you pulled it out, you'd be missing something. What she's dealt with makes me respect her all the more.

—Andy Zatyko

Our collective stories, along with the scientific evidence we amass, form the beginning of a human rights movement . . . Many people are now asking how we can remain alive and secure in an increasingly toxic environment. They ask how we can claim liberty when our own bodies—as well as those of our children—have become repositories for harmful chemicals . . . introduced into the air, food, water, and soil. These are good questions.

—*Sandra Steingraber, Ph.D.*

There is a light at the end of the tunnel.

It took us four years to get pregnant. I became an expert in infertility, but not in having a normal pregnancy. I didn't decorate the nursery. I could not bring baby items into the house. I was protecting myself.

I had three cycles of infertility treatments. We called them "the drugs." Every night my husband injected me in my back hip with Metrodin. We went to the hospital every other day to monitor my blood level and get ultrasounds to look at follicles developing. But my ovaries got overstimulated, which can be life-threatening, so we had to stop.

Then the drug cocktail increased. I waited for my period and went on the pill again. I took Lupron injections for four days, followed by a lower dose of Metrodin for six days. The blood tests and ultrasounds continued.

I got inseminated and became pregnant. But the blood hormone level was low, which meant I'd probably miscarry. I was afraid of scar tissue buildup from another D&C, so we decided to use a special drug to abort. Fortunately the embryo disintegrated. I then waited for my next period and started all over with the birth control pill, followed by Lupron, followed by Metrodin, followed by insemination.

People said, "Why don't you adopt?" But I had a gut feeling it could happen. I'm more stubborn and hard-headed because of DES. I wasn't going to give up. You just bite your tongue and go through it. Every injection, every blood test, every needle, every disappointment.

The third time it wasn't a happy pregnancy. I held my breath for six months. I walked around holding my belly, like it was a glass cage. But I went to 41 weeks and gave birth to a beautiful little boy.

I look at myself as an inspiration to other DES girls. I want people to know there is a light at the end of the tunnel. My son is living proof. I just hope to God he will not be affected from what I have done. And God willing I get pregnant again.

—Robyn Cox

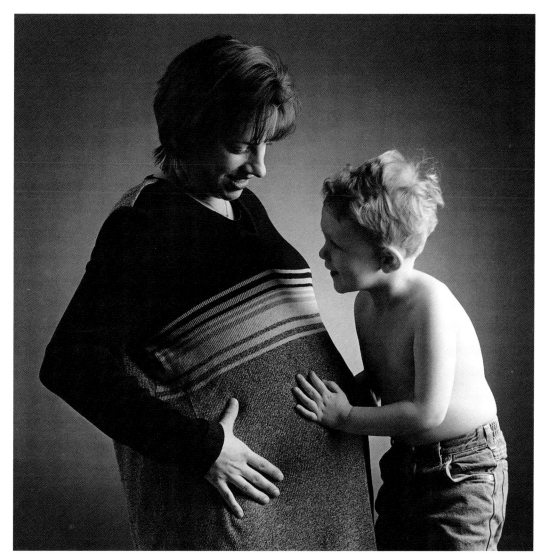

Robyn's DES exposure was acknowledged in her family because her mother talked about it openly.

Robyn had her first gynecological exam, to check for abnormalities, at age 12, and annual exams ever since. Doctors confirm that Robyn's uterus is affected by DES. The left side of her uterus is misshapen and covered with varicose-like veins, preventing implantation of an embryo.

After she married, Robyn miscarried her first pregnancy, and had trouble becoming pregnant again. She took Clomid, then began a series of infertility treatments using follicle-stimulating drugs, followed by insemination. The third treatment resulted in the full-term birth of her son, Jacob.

Soon after Robyn's interview she embarked on a fourth round of infertility treatments and became pregnant. Her photo, with Jacob eagerly awaiting a baby, was taken nine days before Robyn gave birth to a daughter.

Robyn works as a consumer affairs specialist.

DES daughter Robyn Cox, with son, Jacob, age two

Exposed 1965

My roof is falling.
Now I can see the moon.

I was trying to get pregnant after Miranda's birth and it wasn't happening. I started bleeding, but my Pap smears kept coming back normal. I instinctively felt that something was wrong. I demanded a colposcopy and when the doctor looked through the scope, he went ahead and did a tissue biopsy and a cone biopsy.

I asked if the cancer could be related to DES, and all of the doctors said no. It wasn't a DES cancer. It was garden-variety squamous cell cervical cancer. It's possible that my infertility and cancer have nothing to do with DES. I don't know.

Having cancer profoundly changed me. I would never want to go through it, but I think it changed me for the better. Now I know I can make it through these things. They are really powerful teachers. It kicked me out of my life into a new one. I realized the perfect life I was trying to attain was an illusion. It's like the Chinese proverb, "My roof is falling. Now I can see the moon."

I still deal with anxiety. I keep some distance from DES stuff. There's just so much medical informa-tion I can tolerate. What I do is make sure I get the best possible health checkups.

After my surgery I was afraid I couldn't adopt because of the cancer. One day I called the DES Cancer Network and talked to a woman who said, "You know, a lot of DES daughters are adopting gorgeous little girls from China." When she said that, my heart leapt. I knew right away China was the right place.

I feel like these are the daughters I'm supposed to have, which isn't to say that any of these things should have happened. The way DES was promoted was inhumane. It's like the promotion of tobacco, baby formula, or bovine growth hormone in milk. But when my roof fell in, I found a more interesting reality. I think about it when I look into the faces of my daughters. I can see the moon, and it is beautiful.

—Jennifer Little-Moore

Jennifer started having gynecologic exams at 21, and her doctor found DES-related adenosis. After marriage, Jennifer had difficulty becoming pregnant, and tried a cycle of infertility treatments. When she became pregnant, she had an exam every two weeks until daughter Miranda was born at full term.

Soon after Miranda's birth, Jennifer's doctor told her, incorrectly, that she didn't need DES exams any more because only younger women needed to be checked for DES cancer. Jennifer was 31. She was relieved because she did not have insurance to cover the coloposcopy exam.

Two years later Jennifer was diagnosed with invasive cervical cancer. She had a radical hysterectomy, and her uterus, fallopian tubes, and top of vagina were removed. During her recovery she and her husband began the process of adopting nine-month-old Mae-Mae from China.

Jennifer is an art teacher. She is now separated from her husband, and raising her girls as a single parent.

DES daughter Jennifer Little-Moore, with daughters, Miranda and Mae-Mae

Exposed 1961

I felt comfortable enough in my sexuality to turn the abnormality into a joke.

My story is not very dramatic. I have some symptoms. Things I'm not sure are DES, but could be.

I don't remember when I started to figure it out, but I asked my mother and she said she had taken DES. She took pretty massive doses.

I do have children. My sperm count was never an issue. I haven't had any trouble passing urine. What I have is a malformation where the end of my penis has two holes—a regular hole, which is blocked, and one other, just below it, where urine comes out. There are two ureter openings, but only one really works.

When I was younger the double opening was a problem for my self-image. I discovered it and was trying, totally alone, to figure out what it meant.

I never brought it to the attention of my doctors. I've never talked about it to my parents. But I can't imagine they didn't know, having a little boy and all.

I felt comfortable enough in my sexuality to turn the abnormality into a joke. I called my penis a "double barrel shooter" as a way of not making it an issue.

What I notice is there's not much going on with DES sons. Most research has been entirely focused on women. The male side may not be as severe, but we can have DES problems too. At this point I keep my eyes open for information and check myself for testicular cancer.

One thing I don't understand. With the number of people affected by this and the severity of what happens—why aren't more people successful in the courts in getting financial support for their medical care?

I know it's hard to pin down. There were so many companies producing DES. I searched for records but it was a dead end. I couldn't find the doctor. I couldn't find the clinic. This must be what happens to tens of thousands of people.

—David Halvorsen

David started thinking he might be DES-exposed after reading about it in the 1980s. He has had a urogenital abnormality that he's always wondered about. Some of the research studies on DES sons report a higher incidence of hypospadias. He asked his mother if she had been prescribed DES and learned she had taken it throughout her pregnancy. David rarely talks to his mother about DES, though, because he is concerned that it makes her uncomfortable.

David, a manager in the Internet industry, has two children.

DES son David Halvorsen

Exposed 1952

Up until I had cancer, nothing had ever happened to me in my whole life.

I've always been concerned about what people will think about me because of DES. It's so irrational, that people would think less of me. I didn't do this to myself. It happened, and it's happened to millions of people. I never wanted anyone's pity. All I wanted to do was to get back to normal and put this whole thing in the back of my mind.

After I started recuperating I started thinking about the consequences. I had never had sex before I had the surgery. I kept thinking that I never even had the chance to worry about getting pregnant. And I had a hard time dealing with my relationships with men. I was really uptight about telling someone; I never knew when to tell.

Up until I had the cancer, nothing had ever happened to me in my whole life. I grew up with a great family in suburbia, with two parents and a dog and a brother. I had a really good life. I mean you get a car, get married, have kids, have a career, and have a perfect American Dream life.

I keep thinking about the fact that DES completely changed the course of my life. It probably changed the person I married. I won't be able to have children. So those people, those babies, will never be in my life. I keep thinking about what would have happened if I didn't have this cancer. Because of DES it is like taking a different road and leaving behind an old Gail.

—Gail Hyman

Gail's mother remembered taking DES, and she made sure Gail had biannual gynecologic exams, starting at age 13. Her diligence meant that when Gail developed the rare cancer linked to DES exposure, the cancer was found in an early stage. Gail was 18 and a sophomore in college. She had surgery to remove the cancer—her uterus, cervix, and a portion of her vagina. Her ovaries were saved.

Gail married soon after her first interview for *DES Stories*. She and her husband, Eric, were determined to have a family; in a second interview, she tells how their dream came true. Gail's best friend, Geri, carried Gail and Eric's embryos to full term, via gestational surrogacy, in which a couple's embryo is implanted in another woman's uterus. The happy results are Jacob, three, and twins Rachel and Nicole, seven months.

Gail works as a graphic designer.

DES daughter Gail Hyman

Exposed 1966

I always dreamed that, somehow, I could still have a baby.

DES daughter Gail Hyman with children, Rachel, Jacob, and Nicole

Since the day of my diagnosis with clear cell adenocarcinoma, I have been too clearly aware that I would never be able to have my own biological children. This all changed when my best friend, Geri, came to me soon after I became engaged, and told me she wanted to carry our baby. Eric and I were stunned by her offer. We didn't even know if the technology was available, but I always dreamed that, somehow, I could still have a baby. They didn't take my ovaries when I had DES cancer so I still had eggs. And we soon learned about gestational surrogacy.

Geri and her husband are like extended family; we all grew up together. She is the most unselfish, generous person I know. Geri didn't think of it as a big deal. She said, "I have three beautiful children and I want you to experience being able to have your own family."

To do the implantation, we were both put on hormones to get our cycles in sync. Geri was put on a drug that shut down her system and put her in a postmenopausal state. When I got to a certain point in my cycle, they took her off one drug and started another hormone that would get her uterine lining ready for the embryo to be implanted.

I was put on drugs to stimulate my ovaries to produce multiple eggs. Usually, one egg develops each month. Metrodin is a hormone that stimulates your ovaries to produce many eggs.

It's very painful to remove the eggs. I had to undergo surgery with general anesthesia and was in the hospital for the day. They poke a needle through the vagina and into the lining of the ovary to extract the eggs. I had so many. The first couple of times I produced 15 or more. The second time I had ten eggs.

After extracting, they took Eric's sperm sample. We waited three days to see how many embryos developed. Then Geri went to the hospital and they shot 'em up there with a turkey baster-type instrument while she sat with her pelvis raised. She was put on bed rest for two days, and a few weeks later they did a pregnancy test.

The first time we attempted the implantation, it failed. We tried not to get discouraged, and tried again. One embryo took in the second implantation. That's Jacob. The third time the doctor put in two embryos and both took; Rachel and Nicole.

The last pregnancy drove Geri crazy because the doctors told her to stay in bed and she couldn't stand it. She couldn't go out, she couldn't go running. She compromised by staying in the house. She said she got through it by realizing the pregnancy was only temporary, and she was bringing life into the world. The babies were born at 36 weeks and we were right beside her, both times.

I think about the fact that to do this Geri and I took hormones. Why am I exposing myself to more hormones after being exposed to DES? Am I endangering my children by taking more hormones? I've decided there's a lot of speculation, but I'm not going to make myself crazy over something that's not completely proven. It's not as important to me as having a family. To me, having a family overruled any fear of what could happen because I took these drugs.

What's amazing to me is if you asked me to imagine my future after my cancer surgery, this is definitely not what I would have pictured. It boggles my mind that we have three biological children. I thank Geri every day for giving me something I thought I never could have. It's truly a dream come true.

—Gail Hyman

DES *has given me a positive outlook.*

DES has given me a positive outlook in life. It reminds me to count my blessings and appreciate what I have. I grew up thinking I might get cancer from DES, or not be able to have children, so I appreciate David and Emma all the more and get so much joy from them.

When I read about DES, I am deeply moved by what some women have lost. I feel so lucky. There's a whole lot of people in the world who are DES-exposed. We're dealing with the impacts at every level, and for whatever reasons the outcomes are different. DES puts a big dent in some people's lives but barely scratches others. We all feel it, though—knowing it can alter your physical health, or take your life.

For the longest time I'd get so nervous before my exam, I'd be nauseated. I never knew if those cervical cells would turn into cancer. It pushed me into a philosophy: "I'm going to appreciate every day." I try to live each day as a gift to take advantage of, to really live fully.

All in all, I've had a lot of great outcomes. DES has taught me how to take care of my health, ask about charts and tests, and see that things get done. It carries over into other parts of my life, too. I gain a sense of control by being active and managing my health. The way I look at it is that you choose your health care professional. Your doctor is your teammate. If you don't feel he or she is taking care of you, you find another doctor.

It might sound funny, but now I feel I'm over DES. I know it's not true; we don't know what will happen in our '40s, '50s, and beyond. But, for me, a chapter has closed. I've had my children. I'm over the big hurdle. It's almost like I'm looking back now. I'm looking back on being a DES daughter.

—Patricia Miller

Patricia is the only one, of five children in her family, to be exposed to DES. Her mother was prescribed DES near the end of her pregnancy, in the last trimester. During Patricia's teenage years, her mother felt so remorseful about taking DES that they never talked much about it.

Since age 18, Patricia has seen a gynecologist twice a year for an exam and a Pap smear. She had dysplasia—changing cervical cells—which cleared up over time.

Patricia has no structural damage from DES and has needed no medical intervention aside from her exams. She stays current about DES research and found the doctor she sees through DES Action.

Patricia is a freelance photographer and a ski instructor. She and her husband have two children, David and Emma, ages ten and eight.

DES daughter Patricia Miller, with children, David and Emma

Exposed 1965

Even though I don't have DES, I hope to make my kids aware of chemicals.

I'm ashamed to admit it, but I don't know a lot about DES in the medical or biological sense. I think my mom had to be in bed because her uterus wasn't fully functioning, or her cervix was loose or falling or something like that.

I remember, when I was four, my mom staying in bed and I didn't know why. I don't think she complained. She was just so positive. Having kids has been hard work for her, but she says it was worth it. All she thinks is that the outcome is okay.

I don't know what my grandmother knew about DES. Obviously there wasn't much research. I'm not a big fan of people taking things that haven't been tested in a really deep way.

DES seems to be one of those medical effects where you don't find the harm until years later, or people wouldn't do the damage to their offspring. It's the same sort of ignorance as cigarettes. You don't find out until much later, and by that time it's too late.

My mom keeps me up to date on things. She's very interested in pesticides. For years our neighborhood was big on spraying pesticides on lawns. We were the only ones without them. She'd call the company and ask them to inform people about what chemical they were using, and when they would be spraying. People thought she was crazy. But why do people spray chemicals on their lawns? Of course people care about what other people think about their lawn, but it seems silly to me.

I bet my mom's concern about pesticides does have to do with her exposure to DES. We've always been more aware of what we're putting into our bodies, whether consuming food or a medical product.

Growing up with that awareness instilled in me is a big thing. Even though I don't have DES, I hope to make my kids aware of chemicals, and the effect they can have on your body.

—Rebecca Raub

Leah and Rebecca are DES grand-daughters. Their grandmother was prescribed DES in 1951. Their mother, Deborah, was diagnosed with adenosis in her twenties, a condition typical in DES daughters in which cells from the cervix splay out into the vaginal area. For each of her three pregnancies, Deborah's cervix was stitched with a MacDonald suture to shore up her DES-weakened cervix against early labor. She also followed a strict program of up to five months of bed rest. Leah, Rebecca, and their older brother were all born at full term. All are healthy young adults.

Rebecca has recently decided to tell her gynecologist of her mother and grandmother's exposure to DES, so her family history of exposure will be part of her medical record.

Rebecca is in her second year of college. Leah is a junior in high school.

DES granddaughters Rebecca Raub and Leah Raub, ages 20 and 16

Mother exposed 1951

Eighty percent of DES daughters will have a baby. But under what circumstances?

I don't know why in blazes I was given DES in the first place. I had four children and no miscarriages.

Rachel turned out to be the smallest of my four babies. And DES was touted for developing healthy, plump babies. It's left me with a tremendous amount of guilt, enough to hang myself. It was very difficult for me to tell her.

My daughter has had a terrible time. She miscarried four times, then had one live birth. She was in bed for five months because her cervix could not maintain weight more than two pounds. She tried again, three years later, and miscarried again. Then she tried in vitro and was on so many hormones, I said to her, "I'm not sure this is a wise idea."

Studies say that 80 percent of DES daughters will have a baby. But under what circumstances? At what price does the success finally take place? For Rachel, the price was five miscarriages.

This takes its toll on your body as well as your mind, and plays havoc with your career. My daughter could only concentrate on having a successful pregnancy. If you need to stay in bed for five months, that's what you do. And mothers who arrive at childbirth after a great deal of pain don't want to go back to work. They want to be with the child.

I wonder why more people don't get involved in DES advocacy. I say, "Aren't you mad enough?" Or is their fear so great they don't want to hear?

Now Rachel has multiple sclerosis. Some studies show that DES daughters have more autoimmune disease, but we don't know for sure. It's like Agent Orange. Everyone who hasn't been affected says, "Agent Orange is not the problem." Everyone who has been affected says, "Agent Orange must be the problem."

I go to DES meetings. It helps to know I'm one of many. I can see that a lot of people have worse problems. We are really quite fortunate.

—Lillian Epstein

DES mother Lillian Epstein, with daughter, Rachel Breitbart, and grandson, Sam

Exposed 1953

It was 1953 and Lillian Epstein was pregnant for the second time. One day she saw a tiny drop of blood, and called her doctor. He asked for the number of her pharmacy and, Lillian says, "We were off and running with DES for the rest of the pregnancy." What causes Lillian the most anguish is that she feels she didn't ask enough questions.

Lillian's daughter, Rachel, has had in situ cervical cancer and has suffered five miscarriages. She gave birth to Sam after five months on bed rest. Rachel also has a mild case of multiple sclerosis. The only other family member with MS is Rachel's cousin, a DES son.

Lillian chooses not to use estrogen replacement therapy because she believes she is overdosed with estrogen from DES. She is an avid reader of medical journals, an interest she developed searching for information on DES.

Rachel is a medical social worker specializing in adults with cancer. Sam is nine years old and likes playing the piano, computers, and basketball.

—story continued on page 88

I feel like a sister to everyone who is DES-exposed.

DES daughter
Rachel Breitbart

For the past 30 years, DES consequences have intruded in my mother's life, perhaps in a more wrenching way than mine. For me, DES was always this burden my mother had. I basically felt lucky, like I got away lucky, even with my multiple miscarriages, cervical cancer, infertility, and MS diagnosis. But my mother is burdened by having taken this drug. I'd kind of roll my eyes when she expressed her guilt and anger and worry. I'd say, "Give it up, Mom. You took it. It's done. I'm here." I thought maybe it was something she latched on to, to get angry about.

But over the years you get curious. Is something coincidental or related? The neurologist who diagnosed me with multiple sclerosis has 17 patients whose mothers were prescribed DES. Twelve of us have either MS or lupus. He strongly believes my MS has to do with DES. It seems worth looking into.

I feel a responsibility to tell the DES story. I've worked in major medical centers in Manhattan, and I am struck by how many educated New Yorkers don't really get DES. It's not part of the vocabulary. My mother always tells me, "Make sure you go to a DES doctor." But where are the DES doctors? They don't seem to exist, or there aren't very many of them.

I feel like a sister to everyone who is DES-exposed. We all know the feeling of being branded when you're lying there and the gynecologist brings the interns in and says, "There's your classic DES cervix. See the ridge?" "Hmmm. Yes. Hmmm."

What's still weird for me is that I wasn't the one who took this medicine. My mother took it over 40 years ago, for eight months. Yet, it affects my life every day. It's just bizarre.

—Rachel Breitbart

Appendix

DES timeline

The story of DES began in 1938, when British physician and chemist Charles Dodds and his team of scientists synthesized DES from a coal-tar derivative. DES, the first synthetic oral form of estrogen, mimicked the effect of natural estrogen. There was enormous excitement around unlocking the secret of hormones, and DES was considered a great discovery. Until then, estrogen was extracted from animal urine, a painstaking process. In contrast, DES could be made cheaply and manufactured as pills or tablets.

Dodds advocated DES solely for menopausal symptoms. But, by the early 1940s Harvard Medical School obstetricians George and Olive Smith were extolling the merits of DES for use during pregnancy—in the mistaken belief that higher estrogen levels could prevent miscarriage. Medical students further spread the word about DES, and pharmaceutical sales reps boosted its sales. The popularity of DES spread to Canada, Europe, Australia, and beyond.

DES was so popular it became a wonder drug—widely prescribed to prevent miscarriage, given as "vitamins," and prescribed, "just in case," to make stronger, healthier babies. DES was used to treat over 100 conditions. It was fed to livestock as a growth stimulator, then showed up in hamburger, veal, and chicken. It was prescribed to suppress lactation after childbirth, distributed by college clinics as the morning-after pill, given to tall teenage girls to stunt height, and to transsexuals to prepare for sex-change. It was used for treatment of acne, gynecological disorders, breast cancer, and prostate cancer. DES was used so broadly, it begs the question: How many of us are DES-exposed?

In the early 1970s, doctors in Boston identified a rare, sometimes fatal, vaginal cancer in teenage girls. The cancer had never been seen in women so young. The common denominator was the DES prescribed to the girls' mothers during pregnancy. The implications were terrifying. Millions of young people might experience disease, after an unknown period of time, from exposure before birth to a carcinogenic prescription drug. The media billed DES "The Time Bomb Drug." As doctors began seeing exposed daughters and sons, they discovered that DES also causes a wide range of reproductive tract injuries.

Since then, over 1500 papers have been published about the effects of DES. Researchers have found increased incidence of breast cancer in mothers; increased cancer, pregnancy problems, infertility, and autoimmune disorders in daughters; and urogenital anomalies in sons. Yet, no one knows the full story of DES. Fortunately, collaborative efforts are resulting in continued research and education programs. These initiatives will contribute to public knowledge about the lifelong effects of DES exposure.

1930s

1938—British physician and chemist Charles Dodds discovers DES.

■ DES is the first synthetic oral estrogen and more powerful than estrogen occurring in the body. It causes such a sensation that over 200 scientific papers are published about it in the three years following its synthesis. DES is registered for sale in the U.S. and several European countries.

1939—Researchers at Northwestern University discover that offspring of DES-exposed rats develop uterine defects. Researchers at Johns Hopkins University report that mice injected with DES develop breast cancer.

1940s

1941—FDA approves DES for suppression of lactation and relief of menopausal symptoms.

1941-1947—Harvard Medical School obstetricians George and Olive Smith advocate the use of DES to prevent miscarriages and enhance pregnancies. No tests are run on pregnant animals. No tests are done on an unexposed, comparison group of women.

1947—FDA approves DES for use during pregnancy. DES is inexpensive to produce and profitable. It is never patented, so any manufacturer can make and bottle DES. DES use spreads.

1947—*USA Dispensatory,* a pharmacology encyclopedia, states, in reference to DES, "To date no national catastrophe has been recognized, but it is perhaps too early for any deleterious effect on the incidence of carcinoma of the female generative tract or breast to appear."

1947-1971—DES becomes a wonder drug. It is prescribed to an estimated 5 million pregnant U.S. women and hundreds of thousands more throughout the world. DES is used In some European countries until the mid '80s.

■ A popular DES regimen of 125 mg per day, recommended in the *PDR,* is the estrogenic equivalent of 700 birth control pills per day. Some women are given as much as 250 mg of DES per day.

1950s

■ 250 drug companies will eventually manufacture and market DES under 325 names. A brochure for pharmaceutical sales reps reads, "Deal yourself in . . . Play a winning hand . . . Diethylstilbestrol . . . Turn on the stream—and discover how good business really is."

1953—Dieckmann study at the University of Chicago concludes that DES "has no beneficial effect whatsoever on the prevention of miscarriage." Approximately 800 pregnant women are given DES and 800 pregnant women are given a placebo. The women who took DES have more miscarriages and lower-weight babies.

1954—Livestock industry begins to use DES in animal feed to fatten veal, chickens, and cattle. By 1957, an estimated three out of every four hamburgers, steaks, and roasts on American dinner tables comes from livestock given DES-laced feed.

1959—Mink livestock are stripped of fur and rendered sterile after eating chickens with DES neck pellets. Mink farmers sue the federal government.

1959—DES is banned in chickens and lambs but not in pregnant women.

1960s

1962—FDA declares DES ineffective for pregnancy.

■ DES becomes the contraceptive "morning-after pill," distributed in college clinics throughout the U.S. Many young women prescribed the five-day regimen have already been exposed to DES in utero.

■ DES is prescribed to tall teenage girls in Australia to stunt growth.

1964—Charles Dodds is knighted by the Queen of England for his pivotal role in medical research.

1970s

1971—Alarming occurrence of vaginal cancer cases in young women, ages 14–22, puts the medical community on alert. The rare cancer had not been seen in women so young. Clear cell cancer of the vagina or cervix can spread to the lungs, liver, and bone. Despite radical treatment removing the vagina, uterus, and other reproductive organs, some of the girls do not survive.

■ *New England Journal of Medicine* publishes seminal report establishing link between DES and clear cell cancer in daughters of women prescribed DES. (Herbst, et al.)

■ Surgeon General warns against DES use during pregnancy, but DES is not banned.

■ Physician Arthur Herbst establishes Registry for Research on Hormonal Carcinogenesis, an international record of clear cell cancer cases. DES daughters have a one in 1000 chance of developing clear cell cancer of the vagina or cervix. They are at least 100 times at greater risk for developing the cancer compared to a young woman not exposed to DES.

■ DES explodes into national view. Newspapers call DES The Time Bomb Drug. *Wall Street Journal* headline reads Stalking a Killer: How Cancer in Women Was Linked to a Drug Their Mothers Took.

■ Controversy surfaces as physicians, researchers, and pharmaceutical industry question validity of evidence linking DES to cancer and reproductive tract injuries.

■ DES earns notoriety as the first tranplacental carcinogen. First proof that an estrogen can cause cancer; first proof that an estrogen can cause reproductive anomalies; and evidence of a prenatal chemical exposure with a decades-long latency.

■ DES is used for dozens of treatments over the next decades, including: hormone replacement treatment, lactation suppressant, breast and prostate cancer treatment, morning-after pill, treatment of acne and gynecological disorders, for transsexuals preparing for sex change, to stunt or increase height in teenage girls and boys, and as growth stimulator in livestock.

1974—*Wall Street Journal* article reports 11,000 U.S. prescriptions were written for DES in 1974 "to guard against miscarriage," despite 1971 FDA warning.

1975—National Cancer Institute funds the DES-Adenosis study, to follow medical conditions in DES daughters, at five major medical centers in the U.S.

1975—Scientists are able to cause developmental abnormalities in male mice exposed to DES in utero, suggesting laboratory studies may be a predictor of DES effects in humans. A 1980 study in female mice shows similar results. (McLachlan)

1975—Dutch doctors are warned not to prescribe DES during pregnancy, after an estimated 440,000 are exposed. DES prescriptions stop in France in 1977 after an estimated 150,000–450,000 are exposed. DES is prescribed to pregnant women in Spain until 1980, Italy until 1981, Hungary until 1983. Worldwide, DES was prescribed most extensively in the U.S., France, The Netherlands, Canada, and Australia. Dozens of other countries show record of DES use; estimates of use are based on pharmaceutical sales records, physicians' recall, and number of registered cases of clear cell cancer.

1976—Study of DES sons shows 4x greater prevalence of epididymal cysts and hypoplastic testes in exposed men, and more semen disorders. (Gill) A 1984 study on DES sons finds no significant differences between exposed and unexposed men. (Leary, et al.) A 1995 study shows increased genital problems in DES sons. (Wilcox)

1978—Study reports abnormalities in size and shape of uterus in DES daughters, causing pregnancy loss. Daughters with lower reproductive tract structural abnormalities are more likely to have upper genital tract changes. (Kaufman)

1978—DES Action, a national educational organization for DES-exposed people, is founded.

1978—National Cancer Institute publishes a report on DES after a federal task force investigates DES injuries. Surgeon General sends letter to over 400,000 U.S. physicians to recommend notification of patients if they were prescribed DES. No national registry, or program to notify people of exposure, is established.

1980s

1979 — DES banned by U.S. Department of Agriculture for use in cattle feed. Covert use continues for over two decades.

■ Researchers discover structural abnormalities in DES daughters, and higher than average incidence of infertility, ectopic pregnancy, miscarriage, pre-term labor, and delivery. DES daughters who become pregnant are considered high-risk pregnancies. Some DES grandchildren are injured during premature birth and suffer lifelong handicaps. 80% of DES daughters will succeed in having at least one full-term live birth.

■ DES litigation becomes a specialized branch of product liability litigation. American Trial Lawyers Association forms DES litigation group. Many DES-exposed people remain unaware of their right to file a claim against manufacturers of DES, or are barred by states' statutes of limitation.

■ Media headlines reflect public concerns: For DES Daughters a Future of Uncertainty, Worry Due to Drug (*Boston Globe*); The Doctors I Can't Forgive (*Redbook*); Women Reassured on DES: Some Effects Go Away (*New York Post*); DES Victims: Search Must Go On (*New York Times*); Medical Record on DES Emerges After Years of Research and Anxiety (*New York Times*).

1981 — DES Action Netherlands is founded and begins Europe-wide education. Groups organize in Italy, France, UK, Ireland, Belgium, Spain, and Germany.

■ DES Action Australia is founded.

1982 — DES Cancer Network is founded.

1983 — DES Action Canada is founded.

1983 — Anxiety and depression are reported twice as frequently in DES daughters and sons in a medical review study. (Vessey)

■ Study shows DES daughters have twofold increase in risk for dysplasia, a pre-cancerous condition in the cervix, compared to non-exposed women. (Robboy)

1985 — DES Sons Network is founded.

1990s

1988 — A study on autoimmune impairment among DES-exposed people shows higher risk for autoimmune diseases. (Noller, et al.)

1988 — A study shows 33% infertility in exposed daughters compared to 14% in unexposed. (Senekjian)

1989 — European DES Cancer Network is founded.

■ An estimated 50% of exposed individuals remain unaware of their DES exposure. Researchers continue to find evidence of reproductive anomalies, cancers, possible autoimmune disorders, and possible skeletal changes in DES-exposed offspring. Recurrences of clear cell cancer in DES daughters raise concerns. New cases of clear cell cancer are reported in DES daughters in their '40s.

■ DES attracts more media interest. Headlines read: Adult Years Bring New Afflictions for DES "Babies" (*New York Times*); You Could Be One of an Estimated 75,000 British DES Daughters (*London Times*); Diagnosis Meant Fear, Humiliation (*USA Today*); DES Twin Sold in Mexico (*Denver Post*); Banned Drug DES Could Haunt Children of Mothers Who Took It (*Corpus Christi Times*); Suit Filed for DES Daughters (*Cleveland Plain Dealer*); The Shocking Story of DES Sons (*McCall's*); A Private Pain and a Public Healing (*Los Angeles Times*); Manufacturers Criminally Accountable (*USA Today*); DES Nightmare for Millions (*Gannett Times Union*); DES Daughters and Children (*Washington Post*); Mother and Child (*New York Times*).

1991 — DES consumer groups launch national campaign to revive flagging DES research and gain support on Capitol Hill.

1991 — European Commission survey reports that DES was prescribed to pregnant women in Ireland, UK, Denmark, The Netherlands, Germany, Belgium, France, Spain, Portugal, Italy, Norway, Finland, Austria, Switzerland, Hungary, and Czechoslovakia. Personal correspondence cites DES use in Poland, USSR, and China. Other reports cite DES use in New Zealand, Mexico,

Brazil, Peru, Costa Rica, Kenya, Rwanda, Uganda, Zaire, India, Asia.

1991—Study reports eating disorders and weight loss in DES daughters at 4x higher rate compared to unexposed women. (Gustavson)

1992—A research review shows DES daughters are more likely than unexposed women to have ectopic pregnancy (9x), miscarriage (2x), and premature delivery (5x). The risk for a DES daughter's pregnancy to not make it to full term is 3x greater than for an unexposed woman, and 5x greater if she has a genital tract abnormality. (Swan)

1992—Congresswoman Louise Slaughter and Senator Tom Harkin introduce the DES Education and Research Amendment, the first federal legislation for DES research.

1992—NCI convenes the first scientific conference on DES: Long Term Effects of Exposure to Diethylstilbestrol. Advocates, researchers, clinicians, and policy makers set a new model of multidisciplinary collaboration. Research recommendations are made in epidemiology, basic science, clear cell cancer, pregnancy outcomes, and education outreach.

1992—*The Los Angeles Times* quotes a pharmaceutical company spokesperson: "Eli Lilly & Co. believes that it acted responsibly in the development and marketing of DES, and we will continue to vigorously defend that position."

1992—DES legislation is passed. President Bush signs the DES Education and Research Amendment into law. NCI establishes the DES Combined Cohort Studies (DCCS) to update existing cohorts and investigate long-term health in the DES-exposed.

1993—A study of DES mothers confirms a 30% increased incidence in breast cancer, compared to unexposed women. (Colton)

1994—NIEHS holds Estrogens and Environment III conference. Conference concludes that the reproductive injuries found in wildlife and laboratory animals parallel those seen in DES-exposed humans, suggesting that chemicals in the environment may mimic estrogens and harm the reproductive system of second-generation offspring.

1994—Less than 50% of 3600 respondents to a California health survey have ever heard of DES. (Wingard)

1995—NCI renews five-year contract for the largest investigation of long-term health of DES-exposed daughters, mothers, and sons.

1995—Study on DES sons reports three times greater prevalence of urogenital abnormalities, but no decrease in fertility or impairment of sexual functioning. (Wilcox)

1995—DES education study reports that 91% of surveyed physicians know DES increases risk for clear cell cancer, but that only 39% know DES increases incidence of ectopic pregnancies in DES daughters. (Wingard)

1995—DES Third Generation Network is formed.

1998—Cancer biologists question whether DES affects gene regulation and expression, or if DES may disrupt cells' DNA and cause genetic change. (Sassoon)

1998—NCI study of DES daughters finds no increased risk for any cancers, other than clear cell cancer, although there is a suggestion of a possible increase in breast cancer risk among DES daughters over age 40. (Hatch)

1998—A federal project acts to evaluate 62,000 chemicals beyond their carcinogenicity to include potential for hormonal activity. The new direction is driven in part by the lessons of DES.

1998—DES advocates win renewed federal legislation. President Clinton signs the DES Reauthorization bill and Congress establishes the first national DES education program, to be carried out by the CDC.

1999—NCI holds second scientific conference on DES research: Current Knowledge, Future Direction. Recommendations are made for basic research, clinical/epidemiological research, and education and outreach.

■ Reports on preliminary findings include a Belgian study citing evidence of DES in the bones of DES-exposed people over age 50, and a NY ophthalmologist suggesting a link between DES exposure and nearsightedness. Researchers stress the need for further research.

1999—Arthur Herbst emphasizes there is no age limit for the development of clear cell cancer. DES daughters should be monitored past age 40.

1999—U.S. meat shipment is seized by Swiss authorities after tests show traces of DES.

2000s

2000—USDA begins testing U.S. beef for DES, for the first time since 1991.

2000—Estrogen, used in menopausal treatments and birth control pills, is rated a cancer-causing substance by the U.S. National Toxicology Program.

2000—NCI study confirms increased incidence of ectopic pregnancy, premature delivery, and miscarriage in DES daughters. (Kaufman, et al.)

2000—NCI study finds DES daughters are two times more likely to suffer infertility than unexposed women. (Palmer, Hatch, et al.)

■ A Dutch study reports a 3x–5x increase in cervical cancer among DES daughters, compared to unexposed women. (Verloop, et al.)

■ Increased incidence of reproductive tract tumors with no reduced fertility is found in male descendants of mice given to DES (grandson mice). A parallel study two years earlier on granddaughter mice showed similar results. Investigator concludes that in mice, "Increased susceptibility for tumors is transmitted from the DES 'grandmothers' to subsequent generations." (Newbold, et al.)

2000—NCI renews five-year contract for DES research on long-term health effects.

2001—NCI study confirms earlier findings of an increased risk of breast cancer in DES mothers. (Titus-Ernstoff)

2001—DES consumer organizations mark the 30th-year anniversary of the link between in utero DES exposure and clear cell cancer.

2001—CDC launches the first national public education campaign to educate public and physicians about DES.

Today

■ DES products are no longer on the market in the U.S. In some countries DES is still used as a treatment for prostate cancer. In others, it is found in vaginal creams and may still be bought over the counter for use during pregnancy.

■ Clear cell cancer cases in DES-exposed women continue to be reported to the clear cell cancer registry at the University of Chicago.

■ DES-exposed people show resiliency in coping with DES legacy, despite continuing health problems, reproductive dysfunctions, and concerns about the future.

■ DES consumer organizations, led by DES mothers, daughters, and sons, influence public health education and social policy.

■ Many people, worldwide, remain unaware of their prenatal exposure to DES; others are just learning of their exposure to DES.

■ Urgent need remains for long-term investigation of health of DES daughters, sons, mothers, and grandchildren.

2005 and beyond

■ DES-exposed people and DES consumer groups continue to advocate for public education and the promise of lifelong follow-up research.

■ With continued efforts by DES advocates, educators, and policy makers, a new wave of studies will provide information on long-term health of the DES exposed, and offer an important scientific model about hormone action.

Glossary

adenosis glandular cell tissue from the cervix growing into the vagina

biopsy removal of tissue from the uterus or cervix to test for cancer

carcinoma in situ a cluster of malignant cells in the cervix that have not yet become invasive

CDC Center for Disease Control

cerclage a stitching to improve the cervix's ability to retain the fetus to term

cervical and uterine abnormalities ridges or cockscomb tissue formations in the cervix; misshapen, constricted, smaller than normal, or divided uteri

cervical conization removal of a cone-shaped slice of the cervix to destroy abnormal cells; also called cone biopsy

cervical stenosis narrowing of the opening of the cervix

clear cell cancer rare cancer (adenocarcinoma) of the vagina or cervix linked to in utero exposure to DES

cohort a group of research subjects being followed by a research study

colposcopy an internal exam done with a magnifying device to look at cervical and vaginal cells

cryosurgery destruction of abnormal cervical tissue by freezing pre-cancerous cervical cells

D&C procedure, under local anesthetic, to scrape and clean the uterus after miscarriage

DCCS DES Combined Cohort Studies, initiated in 1992 under the direction of the NCI, with federally legislated funds. The DCCS is the largest follow-up study of DES-exposed women and men, made up of prior and existing DES cohorts in five clinical centers in the United States. It is following the long-term health of approximately 5000 DES exposed daughters, 2000 DES exposed sons, and 4000 DES exposed mothers

DES (diethylstilbestrol) a prescription drug, given under more than 300 brand names, to prevent miscarriage and enhance pregnancy; proven ineffective, carcinogenic, teratogenic

DES exam annual recommended pelvic exam for DES daughters, includes palpation and four quadrant Pap smears

dilation widening of the cervix during labor

dysplasia abnormal or pre-cancerous cell growth on the cervix

ectopic pregnancy a pregnancy lodging outside the uterus, typically in a fallopian tube, which must be surgically terminated to prevent rupture

epididymal cysts non-cancerous cysts on the back of the testes

estrogen general term for naturally occurring and synthetic female hormones

hormone a natural chemical substance, produced by an endocrine gland, that travels through the bloodstream and controls or regulates the activity of another organ or group of cells

hypoplastic testes underdeveloped testes

hypospadias the opening of the urethra in an abnormal location on the underside of the penis

hysterosalpingogram x-ray of the uterine cavity with dye

lymphadenectomy removal of the lymph nodes during surgery

NCI National Cancer Institute

NIEHS National Institute of Environmental Health Sciences

NIH National Institutes of Health

radical hysterectomy surgical removal of the uterus, cervix, fallopian tubes, one or both ovaries, and lymph nodes

testicular variococeles swelling of blood vessels in testes

T-shaped uterus a signature DES injury, causing a structural malformation in which the uterus resembles the letter "T" rather than the letter "U"

teratogen a substance interfering with embryonic development and causing abnormalities in the fetus

underdeveloped or undescended testicle unusually small testicle or testicle that does not lower to the outside of the body

vaginectomy surgical removal of all or part of the vagina, followed in most cases by reconstruction with muscle or skin graft

What can you do?

Tell your story.
Telling your story is a time-honored way to heal, empower, and spread information.

Talk about DES.
Put DES into the "cultural soup." Bring up the topic in social, professional, and medical settings. Support organizations and media that talk about DES.

Stay informed (knowledge is power).
The DES story is not over. Stay informed with newsletters, books, research papers, the Internet. Attend conferences.

Learn guidelines for care.
Know about guidelines for care, and the annual recommended exam for DES daughters. Information can be found through DES organizations and the NCI Web site.

Advocate for DES research.
It is urgent to continue monitoring exposed women and men. Contact your government representatives. Support DES organizations. Attend scientific conferences and become part of the DES research conversation.

Participate in a DES study if you are part of a cohort.
If you are part of a study investigating long-term health effects of DES, you are participating in important research that will benefit millions of people. Continue your valuable participation.

Make the connections between DES and environmental issues.
DES points to broader issues of environmental contaminants, because it is a model linking reproductive dysfunction, increasingly seen in wildlife and humans, to exposure to endocrine-disrupting chemicals. Learn about this groundbreaking science through environmental Web sites and DES organizations.

Make the connections between DES and medical issues.
We are increasingly called on to make decisions about hormone therapies—at menopause, in birth control pills, and in fertility drugs. DES, the first synthetic oral estrogen, has important ramifications for our understanding of hormone behavior. The lessons of DES also bear on current trends in mass-media marketing of prescription drugs.

Respect your own experience and your own healing.
Acknowledge what DES exposure means to you, and what you've learned from it; honor your healing.

Find ways to put your DES experience to use.
Each person's experience from DES exposure is unique, and in your experience is your wisdom. Put your DES experience to use in your life in your own best way.

DES research agenda

Basic, clinical, epidemiologic, and psychosocial research are critical to identify potential health risks, and for learning all we can about lifelong risks from exposure.

Key DES research recommendations:

- Follow all generations of DES-exposed individuals

- Increase studies on DES sons

- Follow and monitor DES grandchildren

- Study DES daughters and menopause; follow DES daughters for clear cell cancer risk

- Study the impact of subsequent hormone treatments on DES mothers and daughters

- Study cancer risks in DES mothers, daughters, and sons

- Study the risk for diseases other than cancer and gynecologic in the DES-exposed population

- Study effect of DES on brain, immune, skeletal, and cardiovascular systems

- Disseminate research findings to physicians and public

- Educate public and physicians about DES and risks

See NCI conference: DES Research Update 1999—Current Knowledge, Future Directions, for comprehensive research priorities.

Resources and links

DES resources

DES Stories: Faces and Voices of People Exposed to Diethylstilbestrol
A book of photo portraits and first-person stories of DES-exposed women and men. By Margaret Lee Braun; photographs by Nancy M. Stuart.
Web site features the DES Story Wall.
Web site: www.DESstories.com
Email: DESstories@aol.com
DES Stories
P.O. 10114
Rochester, NY 14618

DES Stories photo exhibit
A photo exhibit of DES-exposed women and men telling their stories, based on the book DES Stories. Produced by Margaret Lee Braun; photographs by Nancy M. Stuart.
Web site: www.DESstories.com
Email: DESstories@aol.com
DES Stories
P. O. 10114
Rochester, NY 14618

Our Stolen Future (Penguin Books, 1997)
A landmark book about the emerging science of endocrine disruption, including a chapter on DES. By Theo Colborn (Foreword writer for DES Stories), Dianne Dumanoski, and J. Peterson Myers.
Web site: www.osf-facts.org/

DES organizations

DES Action USA
A national consumer organization representing DES mothers, daughters, and sons. DES Action works to increase public awareness about DES and promote DES research and education.
Web site: www.desaction.org
Email: desaction@earthlink.net
1615 Broadway, Suite 510
Oakland, CA 94612
Tel: 800-DES-9288 or 510-465-4011

DES Cancer Network
A national organization providing education, support, and advocacy for DES daughters with DES-related clear cell cancer.
Web site: www.descancer.org
Email: desnetwrk@aol.com
514 10th Street NW, # 400
Washington, DC 20004
Tel: 800-DES-NET4 or 202-628-6330

Registry for Research on Hormonal Transplacental Carcinogenesis (Clear Cell Cancer Registry)
International research registry of people with clear cell adenocarcinoma.
Web site:
obgyn.bsd.uchicago.edu/registry.html#relatedsites
Email: registry@babies.bsd.uchicago.edu
University of Chicago
5841 S. Maryland Avenue, MC 2050
Chicago, IL 60637
Tel: 773-702-6671

DES Sons Network
104 Sleepy Hollow Place
Cherry Hill, NJ 08003
Tel: 856-795-1659

DES Third Generation Network
P.O. Box 21
Mahwah, NJ 07430
Email: DES3gen@aol.com

DES Action Australia
P. O. 282
Camberwell, Victoria 3124
Web site:
wellwomen.rwh.org.au/pages/des.htm
Tel: 9221 5077

DES Action Canada
5890 Monkland Avenue
Montreal, Quebec H4A 1G2
Web site: www.web.net/~desact/
Tel: 514-482-3204

DES Center The Netherlands
Wilhelminapark 25
3581 NE Utrecht
Web site: www.descentrum.nl
Email: des@descentrum.nl

DES on the Internet

DES Daughters Listserv
Web site:
www.surrogacy.com/online_support/des/
Email: DES-L-team@surrogacy.org

DES Sons Listserv
Web site:
groups.yahoo.com/group/des-sons
Email: des-sons-owner@egroups.com

DES-Family Listserv
Email: listserv@sact.com

DES Pregnancies Listserv
Web site:
www.onelist.com/subscribe/despregnancies
Email: despregnancies-owner@yahoogroups.
com

DES information from the National Cancer Institute (NCI)

NCI conference: DES Research Update 1999—Current Knowledge, Future Directions
Web site:
osp.nci.nih.gov/whealth/DES/index.html
Research priorities from the conference
Web site:
osp.nci.nih.gov/whealth/DES/chapter5.html

Publications on DES
Series of booklets for mothers, daughters, sons, and about clear cell cancer
Web site:
dccps.nci.nih.gov/ASRB/pubs/DES_Pubs/
directory.html

Recommended pelvic exam for DES daughters
NCI Web site:
dccps.nci.nih.gov/ACSRB/pubs/DES_Pubs/
DES_Daughters/pelvicexam.html
DES Action Web site: www.desaction.org

Estrogens in the environment

Environmental Estrogens and Other Hormones
Environmental contaminant basics from the Center for Bioenvironmental Research at Tulane University
Web site:
www.tmc.tulane.edu/ecme/eehome/

World Wildlife Fund: Endocrine Disruption
Web site:
www.worldwildlife.org/toxics/progareas/ed
/ index.htm

World Wildlife Fund: Global Toxics Initiative
Web site:
www.wwf.org/toxics/globaltoxics/index.htm

References

Apfel, R. *To Do No Harm: DES and the Dilemmas of Modern Medicine.* New Haven: Yale University Press, 1984.

Apfel, R. "Long-term emotional effects of DES exposure" (paper presented at NIH Workshop: Long-Term Effects of Exposure to Diethylstilbestrol, Falls Church, Va., 1992).

Cody, P. "A brief history of DES." DES Action Web site, 2001.

Colborn, T., Dumanoski, D., and Myers, J. P. *Our Stolen Future. Are we threatening our fertility, intelligence, and survival? A scientific detective story.* New York: Penguin Books, 1997.

"Current Knowledge, Future Directions" (transcripts of NCI Conference: DES Research Update 1999, Bethesda, Md., July 1999).*

Dodds, E. C. "The practical outcome of recent research on hormones." *Lancet* 2 (1934): 1318–1320.

"Europe against cancer" (report for the European Commission Programme), DES Action The Netherlands, 1991.

Giusti, R. M., Iwamoto, K., and Hatch, E. E. "Diethylstilbestrol revisited: A review of the long-term health effects." *Annals of Internal Medicine* 122 (1995): 778–788.*

Glendinning, C. *When Technology Wounds: The human consequences of progress.* New York: Morrow, 1990.

Herbst, A., and Bern, H. *Developmental Effects of Diethylstilbestrol (DES) in Pregnancy.* New York: Thieme & Stratton, 1981.

Kaufman, R. H., et al. "Continued follow-up of pregnancy outcomes in diethylstilbestrol-exposed offspring. *Obstetrics & Gynecology* (2000) 96 (4): 483–489.

Ibarreta, D., and Swan, S. H. "The DES Story: Long-term consequences of prenatal exposure." *Late Lessons from Early Warnings,* Harremoes et al., (eds.), Copenhagen: European Environment Agency, 2001.

Laitman, C. "DES on prescription: It's time for Europe to act." *Scientific European.* October 1990.

Meyers, R. *DES The Bitter Pill.* New York: Seaview/Putnam, 1983.

Palmer, J. R., Hatch, E. E., et al. "Infertility among women exposed prenatally to diethylstilbestrol." *American Journal of Epidemiology,* June 2000, Supp. 10, SER Abstracts #38.

Palmlund, I. "The risk evaluation of DES in international perspective" (paper presented at the 4th European DES Symposium: DES—A Drug That Knows No Boundaries, Brussels, 1994).

Steingraber, S. *Living Downstream: A scientist's personal investigation of cancer and the environment.* New York: Vintage Books, 1998.

Swan, S. H. "Intrauterine exposure to diethylstilbestrol: Long-term effects in humans" (paper presented at conference: Hormones and Endocrine Disrupters in Food and Water: Possible Impact on Human Health, Copenhagen, 2000).

Titus-Ernstoff, L., et al. "Long-term cancer risk in women given diethylstilbestrol (DES) during pregnancy." *British Journal of Cancer,* 84 (2001): 126–133.

"Timeline: A history of diethylstilbestrol." DES Cancer Network Web site, 2001.

*Contains reference citations for studies noted in the Timeline.

Acknowledgements

*D*ES Stories exists because DES-exposed people, everywhere, have the courage to tell their story and make a difference—especially the women and men who appear in these pages. I am deeply grateful for their trust and participation. *DES Stories* also comes out of my wish to pay tribute to the hundreds of young women who have lost their lives to DES. Their faces and voices are an enduring part of *DES Stories* as well.

Many people have given of themselves to envision and create this project. I especially want to thank photographer Nancy Stuart, whose artistry and sense of adventure give it soul. Designer Geri McCormick has nurtured and prodded *DES Stories* from idea to completion. My gratitude to Geri and her husband, Bill Jones, for realizing the potential of the exhibit and book. Guy Miller contributed his time and talent for image production, and Pat Miller gave perspective and project management. I am grateful for the skills and conviction of the editors who shaped three books into one: Ceil Goldman, David Pendergrass, Deborah Fineblum Raub, and Jonathan Sherwood. Thank you to Joan Lyons for advising from the start, and to the Visual Studies Workshop. *DES Stories* has been supported by many generous people, including: Sue Benjamin-Rubenstein, the Callahan Foundation, DES families, Janis Dowd, Bernice and Lou Fraum, Sue Froh, Patricia and William Hale, Aaron Levine, Monroe Litho, Katie Morris, Margaret and Ed Perrotte, Riverside Bindery, Sybil Shainwald, Chris Wilson, and many others. My deepest thanks to all who have given encouragement and helped me focus: The DES brunch group, Nancy Dean, Audrey Fernandez, Linda Foti, Sebby Jacobson, Peggy and Peter Kane, Roshi Philip Kapleau, Naomie Kremer, Nancy Miller, Noelle Oxenhandler, Cathy Salibian, Ellen F. Sinclair, the Stillwood community, and others. I acknowledge the physicians who work with DES-exposed individuals, especially Arthur Herbst and Janet McArthur; and the researchers in basic, clinical, environmental science, and epidemiology, who have identified mechanisms and effects of exposure and who have been my teachers. I am grateful to Theo Colborn of the World Wildlife Fund, Ted Colton of Boston University, and Howard Bern of the University of Califonia Berkeley, for their generous encouragement early on. Epidemiologists Elizabeth Hatch, Susan Helmrich, and Shanna Swan, developmental biologist Retha Newbold, and Nora Cody and Pat Cody of DES Action were helpful in reviewing my manuscript. I also acknowledge the support of the DES Cancer Network and DES Action organizations in the United States, Europe, Canada, and Australia. Thank you to Congresswoman Louise Slaughter and Senator Tom Harkin for their interest. I also acknowledge the work of members of the legal profession, who, in seeking justice for DES families, have brought important truths to light.

Conversations with family members have helped me to persevere. Many thanks to my brother, Richard Lee; my sisters, Virginia Nabors, Janet Beach, Charlotte Lee, and Alyson Lee; their spouses; and to Marie Lee, Rick Lee, Deb Lee, and the McHenrys and Ellingwoods. I especially acknowledge my sister Charlotte, whose courage in speaking her own DES story informs this book. I'm grateful to my parents, Joyce E. and William E. Lee, who taught me to put people first. I thank my husband, Chuck Braun, for his caring and his unfailing belief in the value of this book and for the support of his family. My nieces and nephews deserve special mention. During the course of writing *DES Stories* they have given me joy—and many happy stories of their own.

Praise for *DES Stories*

Nancy Stuart's portraits of DES-exposed people are classical, clear and haunting. She captures the moment of human honesty when men and women speak their truth.

> — *Therese Mulligan, Curator of Photography, The George Eastman House*

In *DES Stories*, Margaret Lee Braun and Nancy Stuart put a human face on the DES issue that cannot be found anywhere in the countless tables of medical statistics. By sharing their stories, DES-exposed men and women take the lead in educating the public about DES.

> — *Elizabeth Hatch, Ph.D, epidemiologist, Boston University School of Public Health*

These portraits bear witness to a major global medical event, forever affecting the lives of millions of individuals, and their most intimate relationships. The quiet yet passionate voices speak of profound trauma, and also of courage, resiliency, and transformation. *DES Stories* gives meaning, hope, and healing to people, everywhere, touched by DES.

> — *Roberta Apfel, M.D., M.P.H., Clinical Associate Professor of Psychiatry, Harvard Medical School; co-author of* To Do No Harm: DES and the Dilemmas of Modern Medicine

With *DES Stories*, Margaret Lee Braun and Nancy M. Stuart give faces and voices to a public health tragedy that, while enormous, has remained relatively quiet. Braun writes that "I started out searching for DES stories because I wanted to find my own story in others' experience." This is exactly what has drawn together DES-exposed people from around the world; in reading this book, one realizes that these eloquent stories have meaning for us all.

> — *Nora Cody, Executive Director, DES Action*

DES is a technology that was employed without adequate assessment of its human and environmental impact, and without users' knowledge of its danger. In *DES Stories*, Margaret Lee Braun and Nancy Stuart, and the survivors themselves, reveal with clarity and poignancy the critical lessons the DES ordeal has for us all.

> — *Chellis Glendinning, Ph.D., author of* When Technology Wounds: The Human Consequences of Progress

DES Stories presents a tragic story of how the best intentions of science and medical practice have gone astray. I applaud Margaret Braun and Nancy Stuart on their superb book and encourage as many individuals as possible to read it closely. Thoroughly understanding the "DES story" will help prevent similar tragedies in the future.

> — *Raymond Kaufman, M.D., Professor, Department of Obstetrics and Gynecology, Baylor College of Medicine*

This is an important work in that it draws attention to the suffering caused by DES. Told in people's own words, these stories provide witness to the importance of remaining vigilant in order to prevent any more disasters of this kind.

> — *Shirley Simand, co-founder, DES Action Canada*

DES Stories shows, with art and grace, that the DES story, far from being of historical interest, is a continuing one. Margaret Braun's eloquent work and Nancy Stuart's perceptive portraits gently, but persuasively, bring the DES tragedy home to me in a way that even twenty years of scientific study could not.

> — *Shanna Swan, Ph.D., epidemiologist, University of Missouri*